Briefly Yours

CAT ENGLISH

By The Author School

Published by Ink! Publishing 2022

Text @ Cat English 2022
Illustrations @ Helen Braid 2022
Cover Design @ Helen Braid 2022

Typeset in Garamond Classic 11.25/14 by Blaze Typesetting

ISBN: 978-1-3999132-0-1

By The Author School
ink! By The Author School
Kent, England, United Kingdom
Email: inkpublishingservices@gmail.com
Website: www.inkpublishingservices.co.uk
Twitter: @services_ink

To my mother for keeping a secret never to be told.
To the feral barn cats who've crossed the Rainbow Bridge.
I miss you dearly.
And to the ones I still care for;
you are and always will be the reason.

ACKNOWLEDGEMENTS

To my sister, a love that can't be explained in writing. Thank you for being my right arm during the writing of this book. The love I hold for you will go further than time itself.

My fairy godmother Lynn who motivates me every day. "Back straight. Head up. Walk forward. Never look back."

For every rescuer I've crossed paths with, and even the ones I've not met yet, show the world you can make a difference.

A special thank you to the whole team at Ink! and Literally PR, as without you this woudn't have been possible. Although cat rescue can sidetrack me, you have been patient, understanding and helpful all the way.

And, finally, and no means the least, thank you always to my mother, for teaching me to be a strong willed woman and never judging me or anyone else. I love you and my brothers forever.

CHAPTER ONE

Have you ever had a secret? A secret that under no circumstance can come out. I have. But now I am ready to confess.

I've been selling my body.

I've only been doing it part-time, and to help fund my sister Kitty's law degree. So, justifiable, some might say.

There's another reason I needed to make money. For years I have been helping homeless and injured feral and stray street cats, from my own funds. Often, people don't know the difference between a feral and a stray cat—I never used to either—but they aren't the same thing. A stray can indeed become feral; it's a hard life and strays are often pets that have become lost or simply abandoned by their owners.

Feral means wild, so usually they are cats born in the wild with little or no human interaction. This is the hard bit; they can't be handled, and they end up breeding like wildfire on the streets. It's a dreadful cycle but it can be stopped, and this is where I come in. Feral cats are often forgotten, but not by me. I stop their suffering, have them neutered to prevent them from giving birth on the streets, and feed them so they won't be starving, rehoming those I can. I wouldn't have been able to pay towards saving the lives of so many innocent cats—or pay my sister's university costs—if I hadn't gone into sex work, and I know many of you would do the same if you were in my shoes.

My clients know me as 'Cat'.

*

"Do you mind if Cat watches us today? It's her first shift and she has to watch one of us ladies during a session." Angel pecks her client's cheek before he jumps into the shower cubicle. He's already naked.

"Of course, I don't mind."

"Two for the price of one, eh?" Angel jokes.

I'm perched on a gold-painted chair in the corner of an Egyptian-themed bedroom suite. There are sandstone sphinx statues mounted on concrete pillars and pyramids painted on the walls. Dimly lit spotlights create a false sunset.

The boss lady requires every new girl to learn what happens in the bedroom. I'm about to watch two strangers have sex. Right now, my sister will be sitting in her Criminal Law lecture, learning about *actus reus* and *mens rea*. She might not be there if I wasn't here, earning.

"Just watch what I do." Angel winks at me as the client emerges from the shower and dries himself, dropping his used towel on the tiled floor.

"Where do you want me, Miss?" he asks.

"Park your butt on the bed, honey."

He settles himself on the sand-coloured, four-poster Egyptian-themed bed, head on the pillow, naked, hard-on, staring first at Angel's cream peek-a-boo chemise and then at my black see-through leotard.

I glance at the sandstone sphinx cat statues and think of Egypt. Somewhere in my subconscious, the memory of Mafdet appears. She was a goddess in ancient Egypt who many worshipped, a woman whose head changed into a cat. The street cats of ancient Egypt were worshipped, believed to be magical, capable of bringing luck, held in the highest esteem, although most of them were mainly feral street cats, hunting to survive, and even after thousands of years, feral cats today are still fighting for their very existence. "You can't help them all," some say. Of course not, darling, but those I do help? Well, I change their lives for the better.

"So, what have you been up to this weekend?" Angel chats as she lubricates her hands.

"My sister got married. I went to her wedding."

"Was it nice, yeah?" Angel positions herself so that I have a clear view of her wanking techniques.

As I watch, I think about my sister in her seminar in Employment Law and feel like I'm in another world.

Angel lowers her tits onto his privates. "Do you like me rubbing my tits on you?"

"Yeah, I like that."

"Oh yeah, my titties rubbing on you."

*

It's not how I imagined my life turning out. I didn't do really well in school, but my sister did. In fact, she was such a high achiever that when she was fifteen, she was invited to lunch with the Prime Minister and his wife at Ten Downing Street. Our house and school were not in a good area. There were a lot of teenage pregnancies and antisocial behaviour, so they wanted to encourage those who showed a bit of promise. Mum was very proud of Kitty. Number Ten was gorgeous apparently; even the staircase was impressive she said. Gold stair rod bars held the carpet down and there were pictures of previous Prime Ministers all the way up the wall. Just being there made her want to strive to be something in life. After that, whenever Mum asked her what she wanted to be, she would reply, 'I want to be Prime Minister."

*

"I want to make you explode in my mouth," Angel says. "Do you want oral without?"

"No, oral with a condom is fine." He doesn't want to pay extra for her sucking him bare.

"Let me sit on you then. Bounce up and down on you. Cat can watch me fucking you."

"Yes, please. It's fucking horny that she wants to watch."

I don't *want* to watch; he's got it twisted. I *have* to watch because it's my first day. As she slides down her thong, I'm thinking how my sister will be getting on in her exam. I helped her to revise last night. She'll need to define 'transfer' according to R.3(1)(a) Transfer of Undertakings (Protection of Employment) Regulations 1981. But as Angel sits on him, I'm beginning to get wet.

She goes to full-on kiss him, nuzzles her oversized false breasts in his face, then licks her finger, rests backwards on him and places her hand behind her back, lifting his scrotum to tease his gooch.

"Shit, I'm going to blow my lid if you bounce too hard."

Angel says nothing, just carries on bouncing. Harder. Harder. Bounce. Bounce. Harder, faster, as I move to the edge of the chair.

"Cat, can you see him pumping inside me?"

"I can, Angel."

"Looks good?"

"Looks fab."

Seeing him plunging inside her is making me want a piece, turning me on, as he pants louder and louder.

"You're good at that, aren't you?" I say. The client finishes and takes a deep breath. So do I.

Angel climbs off and saunters to the shower room, placing her hand over the touch-sensitive shower button, giving him silent approval to shower. Her client seems smitten, a shy little smile spreading over his face. She whispers into my ear as he showers, "I made it quick because he didn't want to pay any extras." I get it.

The live porno is over.

I look around the room as the client leaves; it is fit for a goddess. Coincidentally, a male admirer once sent me a painting of Freya, the Norse goddess who is associated with love, sex and war. She was a beautiful woman who rode a chariot accompanied by two cats. In the picture he sent me, Freya was naked, her breasts unabashedly on show. I wasn't entirely sure if he was making a pass at me or not.

"Gosh, was she a Greek goddess?" I'd asked him via message.

"No, she was Norse. She lived in Valhalla with Odin, Thor and Loki," he replied.

"Oh, wow." I sent him a picture of a more covered Freya. "Just found her."

"Great. Nice picture. And good to see the poor goddess has got a dress on as protection against the cold winds amongst the clouds."

"Yes, very true! I hope you are well, dear friend. Hope Lucy [his pretty grey cat] is enjoying her time exploring. I love her."

Then, ten days later, I received a donation from Lucy's cat dad, so I contacted him through a personal message: 'Thank you dearly for sending a donation for the homeless cats. Would it be okay if I get them wet and dry food, as they are very low on food, and I will tag you in a donation post? It is caring of you and pretty Lucy to think of them.'

He replied quickly. 'It's our privilege to be able to help a little. And please use the money as you see fit. I guess it's alright to tag me in a donation post. We [he and his cat] are a bit concerned some might get the idea that we have more money and crowd us for help. But this hasn't happened before when we have been mentioned. So, we guess it's fine. Thanks for the great work by you, kind human.'

He's such a lovely guy. Always supportive and obviously affected by the struggles our feral cat communities face. Like Edward, the blue-coat feral cat who was born in the wild. He would hiss at me but he was such a shy gentleman, so I set up outdoor huts for him to sleep in. I fed him for years outdoors, yet I lost him in the blink of an eye because of the harsh winter. I can't always prevent deaths, though I always try so damned hard.

*

Annual employee beauty conference. Brighton.

"Does anyone know what the original perfume bottle represents?" The brand's co-owner spoke confidently to the large group of delegates.

As the account manager at one of their leading concessions in a luxury shopping store, I was in charge of selling their perfumes. I knew I was of importance because I brought in a plentiful amount of money for their company, but I didn't have a voice back then; I was so shy and full of innocence. Plus, I was in a room filled with celebrities. A famous fashion designer's son stood before me. He owned the brand with his then-wife.

And my gosh, was she gorgeous. Brunette hair, unbelievably thick and bouncy. Curves on her hips, long, tanned legs that looked like they'd just been freshly waxed and oiled to flaunt. Nude-coloured tight suit skirt with matching suit jacket buttoned tightly over her cleavage. She oozed sex appeal.

"The bottle symbolises fertility, it is the shape of an egg, the symbol of sex. This scent is the art of seduction. I want you all to remember that when you sell." She walked forward, holding the pink bottle shaped like an egg in her hand.

Everyone was in awe of her. She was the sex of the brand; she was what I desired to become. I tried to understand why I felt attracted to her, to someone of the same sex. Is it because she was strong, business-minded and beautiful? Yes, but she also owned the room. I knew from that moment on that I too could use my sexuality to get me places in life, to grab the attention of everyone in the room, to own it just like she did.

From that day forth I wore my figure-hugging uniform dress differently; always with my top buttons undone, always with heels and stockings. I wasn't just a sales assistant anymore. I was a promoter of a sexual brand, a brand that let the imagination run wild and free.

Did this brand make me who I am today? Quite possibly.

I learned I could make not only men, but also women buy the product, as a gift or for themselves. I could also encourage them to spend a fortune in add-on sales by making them feel special, wanted. I gave them all of my attention, my eyes staring into theirs while they didn't know where to put theirs. I was a woman. A sex symbol.

I took this whole new attitude with me to my next job, and yes, it was much more fun. No bitchy manager on my case comparing my sales to the previous year; just me looking out for me. So, I guess wearing stockings, suspender belts or hold-ups for work wasn't entirely new to me, and certainly nothing out of the ordinary.

*

"None of the clients need to know your real name or where you live," Angel had advised me on our way to work that first morning. "They might really want to know, but they shouldn't be told, under any circumstances."

"Okay."

"And remember, my name here is Angel here. Right?"

"Right."

"What are you going to call yourself?"

"I'm not sure."

"Something catchy, something the clients can remember you by."

"Erm. . ."

"What name do you think suits you? Something that will sell you. Something that sounds high-class."

"Cat. Cats are high-class."

"Perfect. That's it. Cat."

*

The Palace Lounge is one of the most famous, high-class massage parlours in England. It is one of the busiest and the most exclusive in the city, offering a lot of membership benefits. Since I started, I'm nearly always fully booked from ten in the morning until nine at night.

I've been giving my sister money to help her get by, as university fees are extortionate, and she needed to find a way to clear her debts. Then there's her car insurance. I could see she was about to go under financially. I wanted to ask her if she fancied joining me at work, but it could ruin her chances of having a respectable career as a barrister.

My nerves were mounting on my way to work that first morning. My decision on whether to start selling my body depended on the outcome of my first shift. Just thinking about being intimate with strangers forces my throat to tighten. How do I introduce myself? How will I know what each client wants? How do I get them in and out of the room without rushing them? How do I ask for payment?

All I know is I need to obliterate my sister's debt. It's always in the back of my mind, gnawing away at me, brought on by my desire to better myself and my family. My sister is the first person in my family to go to university. I am proud of her.

The boss is strict. I watch Angel as she walks ahead of me, wheeling her small suitcase, shining with confidence.

"We have to be ready to start at ten sharp," she's talking as she walks. "And the shift will end at nine tonight. The shortest service is thirty minutes long. Don't let clients take the piss with time."

Fucking hell, only eleven hours to go till it's over.

"Some deliberately book in with you for the last massage. Make sure you finish them off before nine otherwise you won't get out on time."

Lord only knows why any man would want to go with a woman at the end of her eleven-hour shift when she's had umpteen others. I guess some get a buzz out of it.

My first client is Moor-Walker. That's what others calls him. Every head-bobbing movement, every eye twitch, is creepy.

"What do you like?" I ask.

"I like to stare. At. You. I want you to always remember me, so I purposely booked in with you as your first client."

At first, as I'm a newbie, it's a puzzle as to what turns a man on, because sex is different in a place like this, but I've got to learn if I want to earn. He takes it extra slow, humping me in five different positions, like he's trying to get his money's worth. Missionary with him on top, staring at me, from the side, staring at me in the wall-length mirror, doggy style, again staring, missionary with me on top and him staring at my bottom in the ceiling mirror above, then back to missionary with him on top. Taking *forever*. He is robotic. Not like sex I've ever had before. It doesn't feel like making love, but if this is what he wants then I'll remember. He likes to watch me in the mirror; there are mirrors all over the place in this joint.

I hope not all my clients are this creepy. I do want to have a bit of fun too.

On my seventh out of seventeen client (yes, that's correct, I service seventeen men on my first shift) the punter meets me in the red dominatrix-themed boudoir. He's a young lad. I overhear him shout out to his two pals before entering the room, "I'm gonna shag her all over! Just watch."

Ten minutes go by. He's viciously fucking me from behind, in our second position, doggy, gripping my hips too tight. Ram. Ram. Bang. Ram.

"Hang on, take it easy."

"Don't you like it?" Ram. Bang. Ram. "You girls in here need a good ragging." He carries on, nothing stopping him. My hands are gripping the bedpost as I try to pull myself away. He lifts up my right ankle, pulling my leg backwards, not allowing me to edge forward. He's holding on to my hips for balance, pushing his body weight on me. I'm digging my feet into the bed, pushing my forehead into the pillow, closing my eyes, waiting for the pounding to be over. I hope other clients aren't like this. His weight is becoming burdensome, he's forceful with his ramming, then he explodes.

"Fuck, the condom has split, love! What do we do now?" Fear hits me hard. Thoughts of catching something race through my mind. I jump off the bed and run to the shower, shoving my fingers deep inside me, trying my hardest to clean him out. Fucking hell, fucking fuck! I'm not on the pill. Pregnancy. I'm not having a stranger's baby.

As I seize payment off him for his thirty-minute service,

I notice out of pity he bequeaths me a ten-pound tip. I feel like screaming in his face, "Err, hello? The morning-after pill costs twenty-seven pounds fifty, so cough the fuck up and pass me the extra dosh." Instead, I'm sick to my stomach and cannot speak. My voice is lost within the depths of my gut. We begin to dress. He knew he wanted to rag me around because he'd boasted to his mates. He exits, leaving the boudoir door ajar.

I walk over to the reception desk and whisper to the receptionist. "That lad just split the condom on me. He came inside me. He was a right cocky twat."

"Angel," the receptionist calls, "come and talk to Cat." Then she answers the ringing telephone. "Hello, Judy speaking. Yes, here with us today are Cat, Rainbow, Mercedes, Angel, Lauren, Denise and Tammy."

I walk back into my allocated boudoir.

"What's happened? Did he hit you? Are you okay?"

Dazed, I sit on the edge of the bed. "He split the condom on me. He was having sex too hard. He bent me over and wouldn't stop until it was too late."

"Look at me." I look at her stern face. "I need you to be strong. This is your job now. You're not going home, you've got loads of guys waiting to see you in the lobby, and they've already booked in. You can't pay for your sister's law degree if you walk out. You can buy the morning-after pill tomorrow." Angel knows why I'm here. I think everyone has their own unique reasons for doing this job. "Right." She was talking some sense into me. "You'll be fine. It's happened to all the girls here. Don't let guys fuck you too hard next time. Use lots of lube. Now, give me a hug."

As she leaves my boudoir to service her next client, I remember the cocky lad in our first position of cowgirl, with me on top of him. "Do you think I look like your future husband?" he asked. Did he hell.

Instead of telling him he must have a lot of people around him kissing his cocksure arse, I looked over my shoulder at him and smiled, "Err. . . yes, you do. Kind of."

"Cat, you're in control," the receptionist shouts down the corridor. "Remember that. And if they fuck you too hard, you stop the session straight away. Wrap a towel around you and leave the bedroom."

Her words make me feel stronger, less shocked, less gutted about the condom split, as I top up my make-up in the lobby changing room.

"Are you ready to see the next guy?" As my next booking enters my boudoir she shouts again, clear and loud: "Cat. Remember. You're in control."

Every person in the lobby can hear, including the condom splitter who's waiting for his two pals to finish with the women they're more than likely still ragging.

A MILF advises me later in the changing room, "Use plenty of lube. Lube it right up, Cat. That stops the condom splitting. Someone should have told you."

There are five MILFs on the Palace Lounge rota working different shifts. This place caters for most wants and needs. On different days there are blondes, brunettes, redheads, curvy ladies, big-busted, smaller-chested, fake breasts, natural breasts, all different ages.

Not all the clients are cheaters—some—but not all. Looking at a snippet of my booking sheet I see that someone called

Flynn has booking slot eleven. He's from Ireland, with a lovely accent, sparkly green eyes, and a freckly face.

His mate cheers at him as he enters, "Wahey. You lucky bastard," gloating at my half-naked body.

Flynn never looked at my face before picking me. Most men walk in and pick a woman they want to sleep with without seeing what she looks like. Some men will fuck anything with a fanny. He's shaking like a leaf in the wind as he exits the shower, a red towel clinging around his lower half.

"I'm really nervous, you know. I've never done anything like this before. It's my mates, you see." Peer pressure, I get it.

"It's fine. It's my first day here too." I smile at him, placing my hand on his juddering leg to calm him as we sit facing one another on the divan.

"God, I'm acting like a fucking fourteen-year-old lad," he says. 'I bet I'll never get another chance like this, with a girl like you again. But I'm married, so I can't do it."

"Oh, you're married?"

"Yes. Yes," he says proudly.

"That's genuinely nice to hear."

"Can I stay here with you for the full half-hour, so my mates don't take the piss out of me for backing out?"

"Yes, of course." I'm relieved to discover I can have a thirty-minute rest break and still be paid. "So, I take it you're all from Ireland. Why are you over here?"

"We've come to watch a Thai boxing tournament."

"Sounds fun."

"Yeah, I'm looking forward to it. Hope you don't think I'm a mug for not sleeping with you."

"Don't be daft. I'd do the same if I was in a relationship."

I admire Flynn for not giving in to temptation. He must have a strong woman for a wife. So, not all men are cheaters; there are some decent ones around. Although he did give himself a toss-off, "to relieve his body," while I dirty-talked: so still a bit naughty.

*

Moor-Walker books in again the following week. The receptionist tells me that just before he left the first time, he told her I seemed a little vulnerable and scared of him. Why would that be, I wonder? His creepy staring, head-bobbing and uncontrollable winking are just as alarming this time, but at least I'm expecting it.

"Do you remember me, Cat?" His right eye twitching.

"Yes, of course I do. You were my first ever client," I say flirtatiously.

As he takes it slow, wanting his rudimentary five positions in thirty minutes, I remind myself I've got twenty-three law books to buy for my sister from the legal bookshop. That won't be cheap. I wonder how many clients I'll have to sleep with by the time she qualifies as a barrister. And now the cats as well; I need so much money to look after them. Is all this worth doing to save my sister from university debt and protect the cats from harm, or will it destroy my future altogether?

CHAPTER TWO

One lacklustre day, my Assistant Manager Priscilla and I were chatting. We were always up for a laugh, sharing juicy gossip and wondering what our lives could or should be like in the future.

"I heard escorts make loads of money," Priscilla said casually.

"I've heard that too. Would you do it?"

"Yeah, I think I would."

Of course, she would. She had that devilish look in her eyes and her perfect white smile sparkled.

Would *I*? Of course, I would. I didn't want to be living in my overdraft anymore. I wasn't completely innocent. Before I had worked at the shop, when I was eighteen, I had been a lap dancer. A look but don't touch job still meant I was a good girl. . . kind of. I was just walking past the club one day when the guy on the door told me I should give it a try. I ended up working in the VIP rooms and dating the owner, who was a real gangster. I'd enjoyed the work. It was the first time that anyone had told me I was beautiful, sexy and desirable. I liked that feeling.

"But do you think you have to have sex with them?" Priscilla asked.

"I think you do, you know. I'm not sure though. I don't think we'd be able to get money off a guy and not do anything for it."

"I'd sleep with them." Her eyes closed for a second then she slammed her back against the stock-room door in a fit of laughter, sliding down it so no customers saw her over the counter.

"Would you really, though?" I was curious to know. If she was up for it, then so was I. If we signed up together it wouldn't be so daunting.

She popped her head back above the counter, all red-faced. "In fact, I'm going to look on an escorting website right now."

"Show me." I peered over her shoulder at the pictures of women wearing lingerie, thinking I'd have to buy myself a few saucy sets if I took the leap.

"I'm going to apply," she said.

"Really?"

"Yes." She wanted the money, but I didn't think she *needed* it like I did. I'd seen her house when I dropped her off from work a while back. But then maybe it was her mum's house. We all had our reasons.

"Apply for me, too."

And she did.

*

We were both given our first escort booking on the same night, at the same time, in the city centre, yards from one another. Priscilla offered to collect me from the small flat I was renting off the council (which I'd only got after I'd been on the homeless waiting list for a year because my mother's partner refused to house me and my boyfriend of the time).

At work the next day we compared notes.

"Mine was a short guy," Priscilla said. "He split the condom on me."

"What? Are you okay? What was he like?"

"He was actually nice. I don't think he did it on purpose. He had horrible brown teeth, though. Thank God he didn't want a kiss. I'll get the morning after pill and get tested. What was your client like?"

"He was French Canadian. He went down on me. Gave me an orgasm. Tried convincing me to suck him without a condom and then strangled me from behind slightly, whilst fucking me, which startled me. He could speak English but not fluently, so we did a lot of kissing."

I hid my laugh in the palm of my hand, checking over my shoulder, making sure no one else was listening.

That French Canadian had paid me over two hundred pounds. Never in my life had I ever held in my hand that amount of cash—especially not for one hour's work—not in a normal job. That was usually a week's worth of work in the store. This money could delete my poverty fears. I had acquired a taste for illicit money. This night was a game-changer in my mind. I'd worked my arse off to get where I had in retail management, doing double shifts each week just to meet the rent on my small flat, all for what? To be overdrawn constantly? To struggle just to survive? Money is addictive, and I didn't want to be skint ever again. An hour's wage as a high-class hooker is more than a day's wage for most people. After holding that amount of dosh, I never wanted to work another day in the 'real world'. I wanted to earn the most money in the shortest period of time by fucking the most men.

I call the world we live in the 'real world' and the sex work industry the 'underground world'. It makes sense to me.

*

I'm waiting in the car, in the dark, for a cat to get into a trap.

"That's the eighth time that jeep has driven by."

"Just so happens we're on a renowned dogging lane."

"Dirty bastard. He'd better not think that's what we're here for."

I lower my head below the steering wheel and my sister Kitty covers her head with a bag. We both burst out laughing, but seriously, it's not funny; it's dangerous, it's past midnight, but we're more bothered about saving the homeless, starving cats that I've been told live in the wilderness around here. We'll trap them, have them neutered and get them suitable homes where they'll never have to worry about their next meal again. We've progressed from trapping and helping cats in our area to reaching out and helping cats further afield. More and more people tag me in on social media 'help needed' posts and I find it hard to refuse.

"Not another one. What's he doing in that lay-by in front of us? Shall I get the trap and drive off? Does he think we want him to join us?"

"Don't flash your lights. Just wait and see what he does."

Clients have to pay me for my precious time. Yes, I will give them my body, but it'll cost them. No, they will not see me sexually without paying me. No, I will not give them twenty extra minutes for free. Nothing in life is free (and I'm definitely not into dogging).

Punters—whether male or female—hunger for distinctive arrangements. Some want provocative love affairs and erotic fulfilment; others are looking for emotional or physical attraction; some just want to get it on. I'm settled into my job as an in-call girl now at the Palace Lounge. There, the clientele visit me for adult personal services. I have a powerful sexual appetite, so why not use my job to my advantage and be paid for having it satisfied at the same time?

I grew up on the outskirts of Manchester, living in a government-built urban area. My father cheated left, right and centre on my mother, which led to even more struggles for us when he upped sticks, leaving us without a pot to piss in. Our household income was halved overnight, which meant a lack of food and no money for new clothes—it was embarrassing. Other children always seemed to be getting new stuff, and we were the ones who had to have free lunches, waiting until everyone else had got theirs before we could even go up to the kitchen for what was left.

I learned that if there was no toilet roll, newspaper would do. If I had no sanitary towels, which was often, my mother gave me a couple of socks to roll up in my knickers as an alternative, and we didn't have many socks either. Teachers complained about my no-sock-wearing, and I fibbed to school friends, telling them I didn't like socks, so I never wore them.

We only had two bedrooms and my uncle lived in one of them with his girlfriend because he was homeless, so we used to sleep on the floor of mum's room. All I knew when I left school was that I wanted to earn a lot of money to overcome the curse of poverty that I was born into. Now I've learned how to acquire it I don't ever want to go back to being poor.

Mum had to support two young daughters on her own. She had a job in a local bar at night and worked as a clerk in the bookmakers by day. My father only paid the seven pounds per week maintenance imposed by the courts. Because he was aggressive, my mother didn't dare ask for more. He'd broken her ribs and nose before, knocked her out many a time too, in front of me, so having two jobs was a must. My sister was too young to remember what it was like living with him.

As soon as I was old enough, I got a temp job at a luxury department store, and I felt lucky to be a part of a posh shop, but embarrassed when my team leader highlighted in my review that my trouser legs were scuffed at the bottom and said that I had to buy new ones if I wanted to keep my job. That evening, I got my mum to sew the hem up because I couldn't afford new trousers.

The managers soon realised that my selling techniques were making them a fortune and offered me a full-time, permanent job. Not long after that, I was promoted to counter manager for maternity cover, but I was still on minimum wage and living in my overdraft. My wage only seemed to cover my travel expenses to and from work, my lunch, my utility bills and rent, so I had no savings—fucking glorious. Knowing the woman who was on maternity leave was due back in less than three weeks, I needed to apply for jobs. I was offered an interview at a cosmetics store and was told that if I was successful, I'd be Store Manager. The interviewer said that I blew her away with my store-operations knowledge and people-management skills, alongside the awards I'd achieved as a counter manager.

When she asked me if I'd be okay with the minimum package salary, I had no choice but to accept.

*

Back at the Palace Lounge, on Christmas Eve, I'm fully booked for the whole day. There should be lots of tips. There are twenty-two slots, eleven hours in the day to fill. The average woman won't have this many men in her entire life. So, from ten in the morning until nine at night I'm booked every half hour. Not every girl fills all the slots on her booking sheet, only the popular ones, and sometimes girls have breaks in between. Men can either phone up to book or simply chance their luck strolling in.

After a long day, as soon as I finish, I'll nip to the supermarket and buy some cat food to feed the five thousand. The list of cats in need is growing, and not a day goes by where I don't feed the barn cats colony and the garage cats colony and the rest of them. I'm now feeding approximately sixty feral cats.

"Get them in and out of your rooms on time," the receptionist shouts.

Some girls polish off four consecutive shifts per week, which equates to forty-four hours of sex. It has been known for the more experienced hookers to do a straight seven-day stint, a seventy-seven-hour week—I'm not sure I could. This job is the survival of the fittest.

My festive client, Samuel, has spoilt himself today by booking in with me for thirty minutes.

"I don't have any money to buy my fiancée a Christmas gift, now," he laughs, apparently unbothered. I laugh too, but really it seems ludicrous that he has chosen to see me instead of saving his cash to make Christmas special for his partner—not that I'd turn down his money. I have her present allowance tucked in my dusky-coloured silky knickers, where he enthusiastically positioned it, and yes, I feel guilty, but if I refuse this money, I won't be able to afford the vet's bills.

I glance at our booking sheets to see that Nile, a solicitor, has booked me, Lusie and Nuria all at once. He comes here every week, and we get along just fine. Nile is an extraordinary client with his quiff of black hair, suit and long black coat, carrying an antiquated navy umbrella with a wooden handle. The three of us must prepare to fully devote ourselves to him for the ultimate girlfriend experience (GFE).

"Cat, Nuria, Lusie—you all have an hour with Nile in room five, Cat's room, as it's the biggest one. He's gone upstairs to take a shower," the receptionist hollers.

"Cool," Lusie replies.

"Let's show him what we're all about." I chuck a smile and brush my hair.

"Show him who's boss." Lusie looks charming in her twisted, golden, shimmery bikini bra, with matching Greek-goddess bikini knickers, gold heels and golden condom bag.

"Where's Nuria?"

"I'm here, Cat, just having a nibble of my lunch. I'm starving. Not had my breakfast yet." Nuria is sitting on a stool in the open-plan kitchen, opposite the entrance door of the premises.

"Smells delicious, what are you eating?" I wonder out loud, pouting my lips at two handsome blokes waiting nearby.

"Moroccan tagine and couscous with salad; I made it at home last night, so I thought I'd have it for lunch today."

"Good idea." Keeping eye contact with the bloke in the leather jacket in particular.

"Mouthwash is needed. I'm sure the client won't be overly keen on a tagine kiss." Nuria laughs, snapping shut her plastic container, shunting off the metallic stool in her see-through red net dress.

"What's your name, love?" The man in the brown leather jacket asks.

"My name is Cat." But I have no time to entertain him, so I go back into the changing room to spray perfume, making myself smell sweet for Nile. I make my way over to the fridge for a can of soda. "Put this on my tab," I say, letting the receptionist know that I understand nothing's for free, as she watches my every move.

"You busy, love?" The man in the brown leather jacket wants to know.

"Can I have her? This girl here." His friend in a white shirt tries to jump the queue for me.

"Who, Cat? You must be joking." The receptionist lets out a loud laugh. "She's fully booked for the whole day. You have to ring up in the morning, or the day before, to be in with a chance of booking her."

"Damn, I wanted her."

"Come back and see me next time," I say, stroking his leather jacket. "Ciao for now." I flick my hair as I turn away.

"Loving what you're wearing, Cat." Lusie slaps my backside as we're halfway up the stairs. She has a thing for bums. I have on a green, strappy underwear set especially for Nile. The material has rouge criss-cross cotton fabric over the middle section of the nipple area, same over the centre of the knickers. Attention to detail is a must in here if you want to stand out.

"Open sesame," I whisper before I swing the boudoir door open. "Nile, how lovely to see you again." He's lying on the sheets, wearing only loose-fitting, blue boxer shorts.

Nile likes to have one girl chanting seductive words in his ear, telling him what he hungers to hear, over and over again; another girl kissing his face, neck, and lips; while the third one sucks him off and rides him. I'm going to take advantage of this and have some fun.

"Rotate the sequence so I can have satisfaction from each of you tantalising ladies, please."

"I like it when a man knows what he wants, it's a turn on."

We're all perched on the divan, Nuria and I sharing a three-way French kiss with Nile, while Lusie has her head nestled between his legs, trailing kisses.

"Tell me what you know I like to hear, Cat." Here we go with his GFE fantasy.

"I miss you."

"You do, do you?"

"I really do." Slowly, softly kissing his lips—this is the sort of thing that keeps the clients coming back—making them feel like I actually care about them.

"More. I want to hear more, Cat."

"Nuria, Lusie and I have been looking forward to seeing you all morning." I interact with Nuria and Lusie by stroking their supple skin for him to watch.

"I'm your baby. You're my baby. I'm so glad you came back, Nile."

"Tell me what it is you like about me. Tell me the truth, Cat." And so, we carry out his sequential fantasy.

"Cat, slide your panties to the side. Don't take them off, just stay as you are, you know how I like it. Put me inside you." He always wants me to be on top of him when he explodes. Lust. He has a lust for me.

Stretching over for my silver sequined condom bag, I tear the sachet open with my front teeth whilst viewing the orgy. Nuria is sliding easily into the rhythm of things, kissing Nile's neck and licking his earlobe. Lusie is kissing his legs, tugging his boxer shorts off. I twiddle a nipple for him, watching him watch me. Lusie and Nuria are both bending over, curving their backs for him to see them in all mirrors, at every angle. Professional teasers, they are.

Some men adore a woman for her heart, her personality, her feet or her freckles. It can be flabbergasting what turns some of them on. He could be obsessed with a neck or an ankle or any other body part. We have to unearth what a guy is fascinated by and use it as a weapon against him, to get him flashing the cash. Occasionally, I steal an orgasm off a client, to have some satisfaction in exchange for all the pleasure I provide; that's not too much to ask, is it?

Nile has booked to return three hours later to see me alone. He arrives carrying a pink bag. He's got me a set of suggestive underwear as a Christmas present. It's astoundingly beautiful. Lilac ribbon weaved through the top section of the black satin bra cups, a symmetrical pattern on each cup. Lilac silky material positioned on the lower section of the bra cups with intricate, see-through, black lace, rose detailing over the top. Lilac ribbon, again, intertwined through the straps of the bra, only stylishly thinner. The panties are matching. Divine. But nothing in here comes for free.

"Promise me you will never wear this underwear for another client, Cat. Promise!" He grips my hands tightly whilst I'm parked on his lap in GFE mode.

"I sincerely promise you I will never, ever wear this underwear for any gentleman, other than you."

"Who is your number one client?"

"You're my number one, Nile."

"Am I your one and only?"

"Yes, Nile, you're my one and only."

"Tell me you love me."

What? That's taking it a step too far.

"Please tell me you love me, Cat."

Here goes.

"Nile. . . I love you so much. You're my favourite punter. I've missed you. . . I'm your baby. You're my baby." He needs me to say these loving words over and over again whilst riding him slowly. The words, "I love you" are precious and only meant for a beloved's ears. But if I don't satisfy his neediness he might never return. I keep talking.

"Yes, I do love you. Your kisses make me quiver. You make me tingle. I always want more. . . You're the man I've always dreamt of falling in love with."

"Oh, yes," he gasps as he finishes. "Thank you, Cat."

As I step into the shower cubicle, I realise Nile has dragged his service out, which has run me over time. He ought to know making me late for my next client is annoying, but the thought of him being more special than the next is all he cares about.

After we've both showered, he mouths to me, "I love you.

I love you. I love you." His time is up. He needs to get a move on. I give him a smile. I won't say I love him back again; I can't be arsed and it fucks with my head. Actually, what's Nile playing at? He has a partner too. He's told me about her. Quite frankly, it doesn't make sense that he comes in here wanting a GFE when he has a girlfriend at home, but who am I to talk?

"You know who my favourite girl is, don't you?" His wide-open eyes search for the answer he wants as he pulls on his long coat.

"Yes, I know."

"Tell me? Tell me who she is? I think we both know the answer, don't we?"

"Me. . . Cat."

"Yes. Yes. You. You. You are my favourite girl. Tell me what I want to hear. Tell me what you know I want you to tell me, Cat." He is keeping my payment in his fist until I tell him I love him. Just pay me my money, so I can pay my flipping vet's bills.

"Nile. . . I. . . love. . . you." I'm in hell's perpetual fire saying this. Even so, I have to please him to get my wages. It's costing a few hundred a week to feed all of the hungry cats.

Finally, he passes over the money and I've no obligation to do anything else with him.

"Tell me more." His eyes seem even wider.

I yawn, as the service has taken its toll on me. He won't leave my room. For fuck's sake! Get gone.

"You're my everything, my world, my life." Where the hell are these words coming from? He isn't my everything and he's certainly not my world.

"Carry on, my sweet darling, Cat."

"I can't get you out of my mind. You're my favourite punter. I need you. I've missed you too much. Oh, heck, is that the time? We must be going, Nile."

Getting rid of the needy ones is never an easy task.

*

Finally, I make it back to the lobby area. "Cat, you and Nicole have a two-girl for one hour, now. I'll send the guys up to your room."

Hang on—the receptionist said guys—meaning two punters together. This should be exciting. "You'll have to start without Nicole, as her client is still in her room. I'll hurry her up." I presume there will be the usual; two guys sprawled out on the bed, waiting. I didn't see them in the lobby when they booked in, so I don't know what they look like. I give them five minutes to shower. Clasping my corset and attaching my suspender belt to my fishnet hold-ups, I'm ready for them, but when I open the door there's a naked, middle-aged man kneeling on the cold, tiled floor, wearing a thick, black leather dog's collar around his neck. I wonder if he had this on under his outdoor attire?

To distinguish my clients from one another, and to help me remember them, I give them each a nickname. I have to, otherwise I'd be confused about who does what for a living, who lives where, who has a wife, who is divorced, and which ones have children. I'll call this one Dog Collar Man.

Why is Dog Collar Man dripping wet? There's also a younger man sat on the divan, blonde dreadlocks, fully clothed in baggy denim jeans and a round-necked white t-shirt, holding a leather whip. I'll call him Dreadlock Man.

"Pay the girl now, you imbecile," Dreadlock Man says, cracking the whip against the wall.

"But what am I paying for? What extras do you provide?" Dog Collar Man seems nervy about spending.

"Oral without a condom, come on face," I say. "Also, anal is extra and reverse anal, on you, that's extra too."

"I'll have it all," Dreadlock Man says. "Apart from reverse anal. I might do anal on you. Pay her."

"And what about your friend?" I'm curious.

"No. He's just here to watch. Nothing else."

"It's a little expensive," Dog Collar Man objects. "I don't know if I'm going to be able to afford it."

"You will give her the money! Or else!"

I cannot wait to see the look on Nicole's face when she sees what's going on. How long will she be? I perch on the bed, only to be grabbed by the arm, pulled and bitten hard on my neck.

"Ouch! Don't bite." I grab his whip.

"Oh, sorry," Dreadlock Man whispers sarcastically in my ear. He's acting like a maniac.

As I unclasp my corset to get my boobs out, he bites me again, on my nipple. What a tosspot! I'm seconds away from walking out. Dog Collar Man stares, smiling at me. What on earth's going through his mind?

Fifteen long minutes into the service with his dominance and there's still no sign of Nicole. Where the heck is she? Eager to make my escape from the room, I go in search of her. It's my room so I can leave at any point. "Back in a minute—I'm just going to see if Nicole is still coming for some fun."

I walk to boudoir two—Nicole's room for the day—and knock.

"How long will you be?" I can see her clothed client sat on her bed, through the partly opened door. It seems like she's finished him off already.

"I'm coming now. He's just leaving."

As we approach my boudoir, I fill her in on what's happened so far. "I'll sort them out for you, Cat." She grips my hand firmly.

"Hi guys, I'm Nicole. I'll be accompanying you with Cat." She recovers the service by kissing Dreadlock Man. She doesn't seem remotely taken aback by Dog Collar Man parked on the floor. Seconds later she screams, as Dreadlock yanks her silver glitter bra cup down and bites her nipple, whacking his whip on the mattress in triumph.

"Stop right there! You've just hurt me. You're too rough! You don't do that to a girl."

Dreadlock repeats the exact words he'd said to me, "Oh, sorry."

"Oh, sorry? Is that all? So, what is it you want today, may I ask?"

"Everything you offer," Dreadlock Man replies.

"Everything?" Both Nicole and I say at the same time. Her eyes lock on mine, as though we can read each other's thoughts. We exchange cheeky smiles, the same idea running through both our minds: money, money, money.

"Err, how much will that be?" the coward on the cold floor asks.

"Shut it. Money doesn't matter. I get what I want and you'll pay for it." When someone says money doesn't matter in my workplace, I take as much off them as I possibly can. Wouldn't you?

He means business as he removes his baggy denim jeans. That thing isn't going anywhere near my arse if he dares ask. It's too big for anal. I don't know if Nicole will take it, either. I can't help but think this man will go all out on her if she allows him. I could imagine him pounding her too hard, whipping her whilst he does it.

"Girl-on-girl, too?" Nicole asks.

"Yes." Nicole makes her move, taking the whip away from him and turning to me. She begins to lick my nipple with her pierced tongue—a new sensation for me. "Mmm, that feels good." I'm discovering a wild lesbian side I didn't know existed. Her licking skills seem to be turning these men on by the looks on their faces.

"Bend over, Cat. Let me lick you from behind," Nicole instructs me. I'm liking the feel of her moist, velvet tongue as she gently licks me. My heartbeat judders for a second and I know I'm going to enjoy this.

Dreadlock Man brings his muscle-bound body towards mine, rolling me over flat onto my back for Nicole to get into this girl-on-girl from above. He begins to massage my breasts then places his palm over my eyes and kisses me full on. With my eyes now covered, Nicole's licking seems even more intense, her tongue slipping between my thighs. He licks my nipples and both of them stand to attention, then he grips my wrists, pinning them down on the bed above my head. Nicole isn't giving up licking, her wet tongue now circling, building up the pace. She places her finger slowly inside me, pushing in time with her licking. A push and a lick, a push and a lick, making my palms wet as she deepens her face in between my thighs.

Dreadlock Man releases my wrists and gets on his knees, forcing himself into my mouth, whilst Nicole carries on, pushing her finger deeper, faster. My body relaxes into the mattress almost as if it's giving way. I dig my nails into the sheets, taking him in and out of my mouth. She spits on her fingers then slips them back inside me, licking me all the time.

"Yes, yes, don't stop, yes, yes, don't stop."

He pushes her head into my sex, making her licks the strongest they've been, up and down, harder and harder, licking and licking, and I orgasm.

"Like that, did you, Cat?" Nicole seems pleased.

For the record, there was something about him forcing himself into my mouth whilst she was licking me. "Did it turn you on watching me lick Cat?" I know she has a boyfriend but now I'm thinking she may be bisexual as she totally got into it. "Bet you didn't think I'd tongue Cat's arse, but I fucking loved it." She's taking it to the next level.

Dreadlock Man doesn't reply straight away. Instead, he changes the music on the radio to rock and then speaks. 'That's what I came here to see, two prostitutes getting it on. Now it's my turn."

I lift my body off the bed. Him calling us prostitutes is accurate, nobody can deny it, but at least I'm a skilled whore. I'm one of the best and I'm proud of it.

"Nicole, suck him," I say.

"Do it," Dreadlock demands, wrenching her hair downwards.

"Not so hard," she snaps back, slapping his hand.

"It said you were a dirty bitch in your reviews." He's starting his controlling again. I may have to intervene and kick him in his ballsack.

After he's satisfied from her sucking he says, "Lie down, now!" Dreadlock Man points to Nicole.

"Sure," she says, acting as though she's fine with him being boss. Brave girl.

He holds her down and goes down on her.

"Ouch!" she screams. "Are you taking the piss?" She launches him off her.

I didn't see what he did—it all happened so fast—but I bet he purposely bit her clit.

"Sorry," he says, not massively fazed by her enraged reaction, moving away to turn the music up louder.

Attempting to calm the situation down, I kiss Nicole softly on her lips and whisper in her ear, "We've come too far not to get paid at the end, so we have to try and keep calm. Just follow my lead."

She nods.

"Do you want to watch us share you?" I manoeuvre towards Dreadlock Man.

"Go ahead," he hisses like a snake, nodding his head in time with the music. The only thought in my mind at this moment is how much time we have left and how much money these guys owe us. I pause as I'm sucking him. If he doesn't have the exact amount of cash, he'll have to leave some valuables on-site, such as his mobile or credit card. Slowly, I keep sucking on Dreadlock Man and he places his heavy hands on my head. He swipes his hard-on across my lips then places it back in my mouth. The rhythm of him sliding in and out of my mouth builds up faster and faster. It's difficult to get my breath going at this speed. He slams my head down, getting his satisfaction out of the deep throat. I try pulling off him, but he's powerful.

Nicole notices his forcefulness and peels his heavy hands from off my head, kissing him as a distraction, placing his hands on her boobs. I knew this would happen. I knew he would become rough again, but I need the money.

"Time to fuck." Everyone turns to look at me, as I disturb their boob-caressing moment. I reach out for the condoms and unravel one on him. He tugs hard on Nicole's nipple.

"Don't do that!" She pulls away from his clutch and fights back, twisting the skin on his chest.

"Do you want to be inside Nicole or what?"

"Indeed."

"Well, be a good boy then."

Both men watch intently as I get Nicole bent over. Dreadlock takes down her thong and sits up straight on the edge of the bed, still naked. "Sit her on that." I park her on his lap, facing away. Her bum cheeks slap against the top of his legs whilst she rides. I notice Dog Collar Man observing the show. Pity for him he's not allowed to penetrate me, or her, let alone play with himself. Must be torture for him. Bet he relieves himself the minute he gets home. Dreadlock Man pulls her down onto his lap faster and faster, taking control. She descends, using her technique of squatting up and down upon him, and he cups my boobs as I kneel beside the pair. Before I know it, he has finished, and she climbs off him.

Dreadlock Man stands up from the edge of the bed and points at Dog Collar Man. "He has a wife at home and she wants him to be embarrassed. His wife wants you ladies to belittle him. You must drench him with the water in this bottle." Is he lying? This submissive male actually has a wife, who wants two female hookers to drench him down? I doubt it. If he has a wife, I doubt she even knows he's here. But you never know.

"Oh, does she?" I go along with the act.

"I'll do the honours." Nicole takes the bottle off Dreadlock Man, swills the water around with that mischievous look in her eye, and squirts it in his face.

"Get on your hands and knees and wipe the floor dry," I order, throwing a towel down in front of him.

"Do it, you worthless slave," Dreadlock Man shouts.

"Anything for you, Master."

"Hurry up!"

"Yes, sir," Dog Collar Man squeals.

"I said hurry up, now, you worthless son of a bitch."

"Yes, sir, I'm sorry, sir."

Later, Nicole and I share a warm shower and she watches me as I lather soap over my breasts. I see her eyes wandering down as I wash my sex. Then she looks back into my eyes and smiles. I smile back, remembering the orgasm she gave me. I'm first out to dry my body and re-dress, as I can't be late for my next booking.

*

I can't see a thing over in the dogging lanes, but cars are driving past, slowing down beside me and watching. I've come back alone this time.

"Just go away." I wave my hand. Do they think I've broken down, or do they think I'm on board with their plans? Well, their imagination can run wild with itself because I'm not stripping off here. I'm back in the 'real world' now, where I'm a good girl.

There it is. A pair of eyes shining bright in the dark through my high beam.

I tiptoe over the grass, getting stung on my ankles by the nettles. I had parked up a little further down, filled the humane trap up with tuna, cooked chicken and cat food.

I got her. She hisses and growls at me as I stroke her head. I scan her and she's not microchipped, so I'll arrange for her to be spayed. She was absolutely starving. Yes, cats can hunt, but some not as well as others. And anyway, should they have to hunt for the rest of their lives?

"No more struggling, lady, and no kittens out in the wilderness for you. You're safe now."

CHAPTER THREE

"Shush, I can hear crying." I quieten my sister.

"I can't hear anything."

"Shush!" I listen intently, closing my eyes and shutting off my other senses. "There it is again." I walk towards the back of the derelict barn.

"I hear it now too. It sounds like babies."

We rush to pull open the barn door, unbolting the top half first and then the padlock at the bottom, which has never been locked but is there to put off intruders. Signs saying, 'Private Land', 'Trespassers Will Be Prosecuted' and 'Authorised Access Only' are everywhere you turn. I can't see anything, but the crying is louder; tiny baby yelps for help filled with pain.

I look down at the ground, skyscraper nettles everywhere. It's the end of a wet summer, and the humid air has blown waywardly and planted many a nettle seed here, and the warm sprinkling rain has allowed them to prosper.

And there they are: two of the tiniest, most beautiful, innocent forms of life. Tiny kittens: one blue coat with pink paws and nose, and one tortoiseshell coat, with the same pink tips, screaming for someone to remove them from the stinging nettle bushes.

"No! Oh, Lord, no. Sis, what do we do?" I reach down and gently pick up both, one in each hand. Both are on their backs, wriggling in desperation. The tortoiseshell baby still has its umbilical cord attached, and there's blood on her. "Pass me something to wrap them in."

"I haven't got anything."

"I'll take off my bra." That's me not caring about being naked to help the needy.

"Someone might see you."

I whip my bra off and nestle them both gently inside the cups. Both kittens fit inside just one of my bra cups. "Which cat are these kittens from?"

"I saw a black and white cat running off as you opened the barn door, did you see it?"

"I don't know. I did see something, but I can't be certain. And if it is that cat, she's the one that's mostly blind. What do we do? The farmer's vicious dogs will eat these if we leave them here."

"I'm not sure. Vet?" I feel motherly all of a sudden. Walking slowly with these two precious life forms in my bra cup; swaddling, protecting them.

*

Only four days before, I had been in a similar position.

"Get that fluffy, white, patchy one!" My auntie shouts.

"Which one? Where?"

"To the right of you." She points.

Damn, so many kittens running around, trying to eat the tuna I'd lured them with, all looking about six weeks old. I'd told my auntie that I'd noticed there were kittens on the farmer's land opposite my house and she'd said her teen daughter wanted one, so we'd sneaked over when the farmer was out. When I put down bits of tuna from the tin, loads of them started running out from under the derelict front barn door, including older cats too. My sister and I had been feeding some of the older farm cats at the front of my house for a while now, because the farmer had told us he didn't feed them, as he wanted them to be hungry so they would turn into ratcatchers. Archaic thinking.

I was wearing some gardening gloves, so I didn't get scratched. Not knowing much about cats at the time, I cautiously bent down and grabbed the white and tabby kitten.

"Yippee!" cried my auntie.

"Ouch!" The kitten had twisted its neck around and bitten me right through the skin between my thumb and forefinger. "Shit!" I placed it down again and all the cats darted.

"You had it then. Why did you put it down?"

"It bit me."

"Try again. I can't go until I've got one to take back home."

"Okay." I placed more tuna out.

"Aww, look at that one—it's a tiny, fluffy, black one." My auntie was falling in love with every kitten she saw.

"It looks like it has an injured eye."

The tiny, long-haired kitten had a closed eye that was leaking water. It was the bravest one of the lot, coming forward, even though its vision must have been impaired. I grabbed it, and again all the others darted. It was suddenly very calm, not aggressive like the other kitten—almost like all the fight had gone out of it.

"Quick, we need to get this kitten to a vet. I think it's losing its eye." Panic mode began setting in. I took the kitten home to show my sister and then placed it on a blanket inside a basket.

"We need to get this kitten some help. It looks like its eye has sunk in its head."

"Oh my gosh, it's tiny. There's an emergency vet in the town centre, shall we go there?"

At the vet, we presented the kitten at reception. The receptionist took the kitten to a back room, then we had an agonising wait while it was checked over. Finally, the receptionist called us over.

"The vet said it's going to be £800-plus for its treatment if you want to keep this kitten."

We stared at the receptionist with open mouths.

"We can't afford that."

"Is it feral, then?" she asked.

What's feral?"

"Is it a feral cat? You said it was a wild kitten?"

"Yes, it's wild. Born on a farm."

I'd never heard anyone use the word feral before. To me, a kitten was a kitten, no matter whether it was born indoors or outdoors.

"So, if you want us to treat him it'll be £800-plus."

"We can't afford that." I was gobsmacked. She said it was a little boy. Bless him. I wouldn't know how to check if a kitten was male or female. I feel so unable to help him.

"The vet checked him over. He needs his ruptured eye removing. He needs to be defleaed and dewormed, and he needs to be monitored after his operation. Are you taking responsibility for him? For his costs?"

"I can't afford to. I'm sorry." I'm not saying sorry to the receptionist. I'm saying sorry to the baby boy.

"Okay, we will treat him then."

"You won't put him to sleep, will you?"

"No. But as soon as you hand him over you give us full custody of him, and you can't phone up and ask about him or his whereabouts."

It all seemed a bit cruel. I couldn't phone up to check on him, to see if he was still alive. I hoped they don't put him to sleep; it wasn't his fault his eye had ruptured.

"What do you think caused his eye to sink in?"

"He was probably scratched by something, an abrasion on his eye, and without treatment, it's got infected and ruptured."

"That's it, then," said the receptionist.

"That's it?"

"Yes, I'm afraid so. Next please." The receptionist peered around me and ushered the next person to her desk.

She didn't even let me say goodbye to the little one. And just like that, I never saw the injured baby boy again.

I have always wondered what happened to him. The little, long-haired, black kitten with a white bib and white paws. Was he still alive? Was he living a better life in a loving home, having been adopted by a caring meowmy or cat-dad? Was he coping well with only one eye? Did he have other brofurs and sisfurs now? I hoped so. I wanted him to have the best life. A life in the wild is no life for any cat. Wondering where their next meal is coming from. Tummies rumbling for days on end.

Eating out of rubbish bins. Drinking out of dirty puddles. I couldn't have the other ones at the derelict barn starving. I didn't even know how many more there were there. I needed to investigate.

*

Fresh from the pet shop and armed with some new bowls, cat food and bottled water, my sister and I decide to approach the old barn with the caved-in roof, to attempt to help this fluffy family. After trudging through the snow and carefully making our way through abandoned cars, fly-tipped rubbish, broken glass and scrap metal, we arrive. What happens next changes my life. Fur-ever.

As my torch lights up the inside of the old building through the broken window, there is a sudden scurry of panic as at least fifteen petrified cats dart away. Scattered amongst the wooden beams and junk are at least another fifteen pairs of gleaming eyes reflecting back at us. I guess they are the less nervous moggies who have stayed where they were to see who has come to disturb them. I turn around to face my sister.

"This isn't a family. It's a whole community!"

"There must be thirty to forty cats!"

"How do we feed thirty to forty cats?"

"That's just what I've seen; there could be double that."

"They must be breeding like crazy!"

"What on earth are we going to do?"

"We need to help these cats, and quickly."

The next morning, we ring a local cat charity to tell them

about the problem. They say they will lend us a trap, as this is the only way we can catch the feral cats for the trapping and neutering, often referred to as trap, neuter, return (TNR) in the world of cat rescue.

We are told that if—or when—we successfully trap a cat, we will have to contact them again and possibly, depending on their circumstances, they will give us vouchers to pay for the neutering operations. They tell us to advise the vet to ear tip (cut the tip of the ear off) of each cat we have neutered because there are so many, and we need to distinguish which have been done and which haven't. We don't want to be sending cats back to the vet that have already been fixed. The cat charity will also include a deflea and deworm.

Thankfully, the cat charity helps us neuter and spay a few, but then when we phone their helpline for further assistance, they tell us their funding has been cut for feral cats, so they can't offer us any more neutering vouchers, but they explained if the cats weren't feral and living indoors, they'd be able to help. This is a complete mystery to me. If the streets are full of feral cats running around, breeding, surely that makes for an immense problem?

So, the onus is on me to pay for the operations, to stop the feral cat community from breeding. If cash is low, I can't go out on any trapping missions: if I trap a cat, who will pay for the operation, the deflea and deworming medication? It would be pointless.

Trapping isn't easy because often I inadvertently trap the ones I'd already ear tipped, so it takes time and patience. One by one, I get them all neutered, and the marvellous drop-trap donated by a kind cat friend works wonders. If an ear-tipped cat goes into the trap, I don't pull the trap string to drop it closed. That way, I can just help the cats that need it. It takes lots of dedication, and sometimes means being out past midnight, but eventually I start to see the light at the end of the tunnel. I even start naming the feral cats and, using social media, I ask the public to help me choose names. The cats may be feral, but they still deserve love, and a name is the first step.

*

How can this be? Two new kittens have been spotted near the derelict barn where the feral barn cats live. They seem to be following Tiger Lily so she must be their mummy.

One of the kittens is ginger and one is a long-haired calico tortoiseshell. They could be a boy and a girl or both girls, but the ginger gene, which produces the orange colour, is carried on the X chromosome. Females have two X chromosomes and so need two copies of this gene to become ginger, whereas males only need one. This means there are roughly three ginger toms to each female ginger kitty, so I'm guessing this ginger kitten is more likely to be a boy. Tortoiseshell and calico (white, orange and black) cats are apparently mostly female so no doubt this little calico fluffball is a little girl. As soon as we can, we will trap them for neutering.

The ginger and the calico seem to have taken to hiding out in a rotten side shed next to the derelict barn and have only been spotted since their mother stopped feeding them milk and they've had to look for their own food. Now I know where they sleep, I hope they'll be easy to trap. I pray that they can be rehomed, if they're not too feral already. I don't have names for them yet, plus I am broke at the moment, as work isn't always regular.

*

I'm terrified someone may find out my secret, and I know that I have to take matters into my own hands. I deactivate my personal social media account, feeling I have no choice. If I quit my job through fear of being discovered then I won't be able to afford to TNR, feed the cats or carry on helping my sister with her studies, travel expenses to and from university and her lunches. I've had to tax and insure my car and get it serviced. There's the monthly rent, gas, electric and water bills. I have to buy food, pay for her stationery and law books. She needed a laptop for research and to type up essays, plus a printer to print them on. I have to buy lined paper for her to write notes on, plain paper to print on, and files. Fuck me, the list is endless. My mum can't help, she barely gets by, with my three younger brothers to care for. I give them all money to get by too. I have a huge responsibility on my shoulders.

Some of my sister's fellow students seem unduly interested in what she does for an occupation. Nosy buggers.

"Do you work?" her classmate Natalie asks her.

"No."

"How did you afford to buy the full list of law books, then?"

Then another student, Anna, asks, "How can you afford to drive and pay for parking on campus? It's a rip-off. I catch the train then the bus here."

"I catch the train, then the tram five days a week," Natalie butts in again.

I can see why they might be curious but she's not exactly going to tell them her sister fucks for a living to help her study. Her classmates are living at their parents' homes, working weekends, even missing lectures and revision classes to keep a minimum wage job in order to get by.

Kitty admitted to me she told them our mother took out bank loans for her.

The fact that mum knows about my secret is some consolation. I don't have to hide it from her like I hide it from everyone else. Our mother is one of the strongest and least judgemental people I have ever met, which is maybe why she kept choosing men who let her down. She's too quick to give people the benefit of the doubt, and people have abused it.

Early on, in fact just on my second shift as a call girl, a client who calls himself Andy Pandy told me straight, "In life you'll come to realise that men don't want children. It's women who want children. Men only love and want sex, but obviously that creates children."

That's the reason why massage parlours are so successful: they supply males with no-strings sex.

Andy Pandy once played for a famous English rugby team. Now he's retired and owns a supercar, or so he tells me. He doesn't tell me that he's married with a young daughter, but Angel does. She's fucked him too. I guess when men are trying to make themselves appealing, they only tell what they think the other person wants to hear. And, so the saying goes, women fall in love with what they hear, but men fall in love with what they see. Another reason why brothels do so well.

During Andy Pandy's first booking with me we didn't even get it on. He told me he couldn't because I was too pretty and it was intimidating, so he was flopping. Tipping me, he reassured me he was going to return to give me his number so we could go out for 'fine dining', as he called it. As if I'd want to date any guy who visits a parlour every week without fail, no thank you. I wonder if his wife knows about his visits. No, is likely to be the answer, otherwise he'd probably not be back.

One week later he did drop off his number, but a girl I was working with kindly warned me he'd previously dated another girl here and ripped her off royally. He'd borrowed thousands off her, saying he'd repay her, but didn't pay her back, probably because he knew she'd be too scared to demand the money back. . . and she was.

He visits for a third time a month later. As soon as I walk in, he growls, "So, where was my phone call, eh?" He sounds aggressive. I cannot tell him that I've been told he's a rip-off merchant. Instead, I tell a little lie, "It's nothing against you, but it wouldn't feel right dating a guy I've met in here."

Sicilia, one of the ladies who's worked here for donkeys' years, made a client fall for her who then went on to create a website for the sex industry that rated various working girls, probably so he could keep an eye on what the punters were saying. The website is renowned. Punters can write reviews on women working in massage parlours throughout the United Kingdom. The website chat room provides detailed client experiences, from who offers the best blow jobs to who offers the best girlfriend experience, helping others pick and choose who to fuck in the future.

"Well, obviously it can't be anything to do with my looks," he says, lying there, showing off his hard-on. The pompous prick truly believes he's God's gift to women. I'd love to give him a few home truths here and now. The fact he's an ex-rugby player who owns a supercar doesn't make me wet. To me, he is just another wife-cheater and a thieving crook.

*

My mobile chimes from behind the reception desk. It sounds as though I've received a text message. Best go and check. Yes, it's a message from my sister forwarding me a reply from her Intellectual Property Law lecturer.

Your application was successful, and you will be marshalling His Honour Judge Blane at Manchester Crown Court on the 6th and 8th. Please wear smart business dress, arriving sharpish at 9.00 am at the court main entrance reception area, where the Supervising Usher will accompany you to Judge Blane's chamber.

Remember, you are representing our university at all times, and we have an outstanding rapport with the Supervising Usher from previous years, so we expect to receive only positive feedback from the Supervising Usher this year.

I'm elated at her application being accepted to Marshall a judge. Whilst waiting for my next client, Ryan, to arrive, I internet search the postal code of Manchester Crown Court. I need to know the exact road it's on because I want to be the one to take her to Marshall the judge, how exciting. Selecting 'Images' to see what the building looks like; I scroll through pictures. My heart stops as the face of one of my regular clients appears. It's Adam, nickname Shining Star. He never told me his real name, only that in his culture it means 'shining star', and always gave the name Adam when booking in. Online, under his picture, it states, 'Convicted at Manchester Crown Court. Death by Dangerous Driving.' So, it was true what he'd told me. I'd previously questioned why his physique was so impeccably muscular, and he'd told me he'd spent much of his adolescent life in prison, going to the prison gym for something to do, but he never told me why. Maybe he was ashamed he'd killed someone.

Now, all that's running through my mind is what if I bump into any clients whilst I'm dropping my sister off? The last thing I want is to be outed in those circumstances. What would I say? Would I keep quiet or speak up? Would I run and hide or stand my ground? My sister was thrilled to be chosen but now I'm having second thoughts about supporting her in person. It is what it is, though. I must still help her. Her not turning up after she's been given the opportunity would be daft. Many students applied and she was selected, amongst a few others, so her application must have shone. She has to go. I just pray I don't get spotted.

My brain goes into overdrive. The judge she's Marshalling could even be my client. What if one of my clients works as a security guard at the court, or a solicitor? Not all of them divulge their occupations to me. How will I be able to avoid clients in public places? I've even thought about cutting my hair short after leaving the sex industry, or dyeing it a different colour, so I'm not easily recognisable. I don't know if this would work, though. I can't go on being afraid forever. I've got to fight my fears and think of my sister's future career. Apparently, Kitty needs to have 'Marshalling a High Court judge' on her CV, so when she applies to do a Master's in Law on the Bar Professional Training Course (BPTC) she'll have better chance of acceptance. Maybe she'll look after me one day like I look after her.

*

"There's a woman named Magdalena who runs her own small cat charity not too far away. I was talking to her and she said she can get a quick appointment for cats to be neutered. Our vet is fully booked for neutering over the next few weeks. She said she'll transport them because the vet knows her and not us. The two kittens and Tiger Lily need to be neutered," I tell my sister.

"She's asking to come to the feral cat colony."

"I don't like the idea of someone else knowing where the feral cats live. What if she traps them all without us knowing and takes them all away? They're all family there. We can't take them away from each other. They might not cope well in homes," says my sister.

"I thought about that, but I had no choice but to tell her their location, because they need neutering now so they don't start breeding."

"So, I'll trap them all and once that's done, I've got to phone her."

I position a trap (with tuna inside) within the grassy area where Tiger Lily hangs around with her two kittens. Much to my surprise, she hops in the trap. To make sure she would be hungry, I hadn't put out any food for her the day before. It makes enticing them into the trap that much easier, but it isn't a guarantee.

But there's a problem. "Sorry, I can't collect the female feral cat off you today or tonight. The vet I use has no space for any operations this week." Oh, great. Magdalena can't help, so I'm stuck having to spend my weekly food money on booking Tiger Lily in at our local vet. "If you can catch the two kittens early next week, the vet I use will have space."

I just have to hope Magdalena isn't messing me about.

Early the next morning I plan to try to catch Tiger Lily's kittens from the same place. Even if Magdalena says she can't fit them in at her vet, I can't just leave two vulnerable kittens outside alone without their mum for protection. The other cats in the colony won't guard or protect the newcomers because of Tiger Lily's position as an outsider. Tiger Lily is a rejected member of the homeless barn cat colony. Whenever she goes to eat at the feeding stations, the other cats chase her away. Because of this territorial bullying, she resides in a different area, away from the main colony. I don't know why she was cast out but right now, what I do know, is that these kittens might not get any food and could be attacked by roaming males, so catching them is my number one priority.

Unfortunately, I can't trap her kittens though. Having no mum for protection seems to have put them on edge, and they aren't coming out of the rotten shed they live in or going anywhere near the trap. But I must keep trying—I won't give up on them.

Thankfully, soon Tiger Lily is healing well after her spay. The vet tipped her left ear, so now it's clear she's feral. She's kept in for observation then I release her back in the wild to the area where her kittens are and put down food for them all. She must have been happy to be back out there with them—they're all she has since she was rejected by the colony. She has never had any other cats for company or any love, so even though I was distraught at seeing two new kittens, I knew they were meant to be here. Now Tiger Lily has her own little family, and she doesn't have to be lonely anymore. And if I work to feed her and the others, hopefully they'll have a good quality of life. . . and no more kittens!

*

About a month later (yes, a month, that's honestly how long it took me) by some miracle I manage to trap the long-haired calico kitten. She is stunning. Then, later that night, I got the ginger kitty as well. "I'm on a roll." Thankfully, Magdalena's vet has space for them both and she comes to collect them. She's been in cat rescue for many years and is a stern woman. She doesn't even give the youngsters a second look as she places them in the back of her white van. I give her my address to drop them back off with me, so I can keep them indoors until they recover. I watch as she drives away with them into the night. It's always a worry about how operations will go. These cats aren't mine, but I do still care for them, wanting fast recoveries for them all with no complications or infections. They deserve to be healthy at least.

Magdelena calls me the next day. "They've both had their operations this morning. Will you be around this evening for me to drop them off at yours?"

"Yes, of course, but I was thinking. . . because these cats are still young, I'd like to bring them inside whilst they're healing after their operations and see if I can socialise them. Maybe make them less feral?" There is a pause of silence at the end of the phone.

"What do you mean?" she finally mumbles.

"If I can make them less feral, then I can rehome them both, hopefully together, and then they can have a better life. Being outdoors is tough on them, and winter isn't far away."

Magdalena snorts. "I wouldn't bother if I were you."

I sigh. It's really not her decision. I carry on.

"I can meet you this evening at the colony at about seven o'clock, if that's a good time for you, Magdalena?"

"About ten o'clock is better for me. See you then?"

"Okay. Oh, Magdalena—what gender are they?"

"Ginger one's a boy. Calico is a girl." As we thought.

"Aww, that's lovely. I'll have to name them."

"You name them?" She seems surprised.

"Yes."

She laughs down the phone. "See you later." She hangs up still laughing.

Why does naming them sound so ludicrous to her? I name all the feral cats I feed, partly so I can distinguish them from each other, but also so they can have a place and a purpose on this earth. If they mean something to someone then they're not just another number.

Later that evening, I'm waiting near the colony for Magdalena to turn up. It's pitch black. My phone rings. "Hi, Magdalena."

"I've released the two cats and I'm on my way home." My blood runs cold.

"What?"

"Gregory opened their cages in the back of the van and

let them out where we met you the other night." My heart is beating fast —I can't believe what she's saying.

"But I gave you my address and told you I was going to keep them indoors until they recovered, keep an eye on them."

"Yes, but I forgot. I mean, Gregory forgot. Not to worry, they're back where you found them now. Let me know if you need help neutering again and if I can help, I will."

I am starting to panic.

"I just wanted to keep an eye on them after their operations. Did they go well? Are they both okay?"

"The ginger boy is still drowsy after the op." She hangs up the phone. My panic is replaced by anger. Who the hell does she think she is? How dare she release them without me even looking at them first? What does she mean, the ginger one is still drowsy? In that moment, I hate her. We're going to have to try and trap them again and bring them indoors, but it took us a month to catch them in the first place. I look around, but there's no sign of them. I phone my sister.

"Sis, have you got the kittens?"

"Fucking Magdalena has let them back outside."

"What?"

"I'm absolutely fuming. I think she's done it on purpose. I mean, when I mentioned I wanted to take them in so I could try to tame them she didn't seem to agree."

"She's old school. So, have you not seen them at all?"

"No, and Magdalena said the ginger boy is still drowsy." My sister clearly feels the same way as I do. "It's so wrong of her to release them like this," she says.

"I can't believe she's done this, you know. I can't see them anywhere. It's too dark."

"Don't stay out there, it's late—it's not safe for you on your own. Go back home and try and see if you can find them both tomorrow."

*

Weeks pass and I keep trying to catch a glimpse of the youngsters. While I wait, I write a social media post:

Please help name us! We don't have names yet because we've only just been discovered, but I'm a ginger boy aged about five months old and my sister is a calico girl. You can suggest any names you like and write a number on the list below by commenting on this post. Our helpers will update the list, randomly select two lucky numbers from a draw, and notify everyone of the winning names once all slots have been filled.

We have a lovely, overwhelming response to the naming draw, so I decide to draw out two for each kitty, giving four lucky winners the chance of naming the feral kittens with first and middle names. The calico girl's new name is Cassandra-Dior and her brother is Leo-Nigel.

*

Kitty is dressed in a grey suit with a mid-length skirt, white shirt and fitted jacket and she looks the part. She asked me to walk in with her, as she felt so nervous about her big break, so we head up the concrete stairs that lead to the Crown Court main entrance together, before she meets the Supervising

Usher. A few students are also seated in the court foyer area, so we walk towards them.

"Wow, you look nice. Love your suit. Bet that was expensive," one of her classmates greets her, looking her up and down.

"Thanks. Did you get here okay?"

"My dad dropped me off. I don't drive yet. There's no parking round here anyway. Did you drive here today in that beautiful sports car? Is it yours?'

"Yes, it's my sister's car. Oh, look, I think that's the Supervising Usher. We'd best stand up to greet her."

The Supervising Usher calls out names and I say goodbye to Kitty and proudly walk off. She said she'll only be a couple of hours before her dinner break, so I'll wait in the courthouse foyer.

I know there aren't many female judges, but I truly believe that she can reach her dreams. I feel that the law world could be her oyster. I notice a middle-aged man gawping at me as I sit down outside the courtroom to use my phone. I sip some bottled water as if nothing is wrong. His presence becomes more noticeable, non-stop staring, so I stare back at him.

Like Kitty, he's wearing a grey suit. He must be attending a courtroom here. He does look familiar. Is he from her university? No, he's not a student or he wouldn't be sat here waiting like me. Oh, fuck! He saw me a couple of months ago as a client. He had sex with me. Shock slaps me across the face. This is exactly what I was afraid of.

His left eyebrow begins to rise as he keeps staring at me. He recognises me. He must do, or else he'd look elsewhere, and stop fucking gawping straight into my eyes. I stand up, walking away from him towards a sign, which points to the female toilets. I'm not sitting there whilst he keeps staring. No way. He's not a regular client of mine. I've only sexed with him once. I don't owe him any recognition. Maybe he assumes I'm attending court, as he is. Maybe he's a witness to a major case, or maybe he's a defendant. Maybe he thinks I'm a defendant. Well, I'm not. I've never committed a criminal offence. Being a call girl doesn't make me a criminal.

Gazing at my shaken reflection in the mirror I tell myself I have to go back outside. I'm not hiding anymore. I'm fed up with hiding. I stride back out.

He's gone. But he wasn't a mirage, I saw him all right. Possibly he was embarrassed too. After all, he had to pay me for my time. Will my future always be like this? Living in fear that I might be spotted; then, when I am spotted, having to run away, hiding in toilets, feeling ashamed of how I earn a living? I pray not.

*

The kittens are nowhere to be seen, and I come to the realisation that I won't be able to trap them again. The last sighting was when I had seen the ginger boy come for food at one of the feeding stations a few days after his operation. I was so elated to see that Beauty; a partially blind girl was allowing him to eat from the food bowl beside her. She seemed to have accepted his presence. But I hadn't seen them in about three months.

"Sis, I think tomorrow we need to go looking on the farmer's land for Tiger Lily's kittens."

"They're probably dead. You should have fed them in front of that rotten shed they lived in with their mummy cat."

"Don't blame me," I reply. "Magdalena was the one who released them. I was going to try and help them get new homes. I wanted them to have a better life. You could've fed them and put down water where they lived too. You know the colony have rejected their mum. I bet the colony rejected them too."

We both knew we weren't responsible, but it still hurt, and we were taking it out on each other.

"There's food at all the other feeding stations. You know full well the farmer said he didn't want us going to the locked-off area where that shed is."

"I bet someone fed them kebab meat. I keep seeing empty takeaway boxes in that area. Someone could've killed them." Cats can't eat garlic or onions. They can't eat any bulbs—tulips aren't safe for cats to eat, either.

"Look, we can't blame anyone for anything yet," my sister says, trying to calm me and make me see sense. "But I bet that fucking Magdalena has come back and trapped them again and taken them away. I knew we shouldn't have told her where the colony lives." And there she goes, blaming other people again, like me. We couldn't help it—we were both in despair.

The next day we decide to go and look for the kittens together. What we saw made us feel sick.

"What the hell?"

"Shush, we can't be seen here." On the farmer's land we immediately see a handwritten sign on the rotten shed rear door: RAT POISON.

"Maybe the farmer put the sign up to deter people from coming on his land?"

I can't see any sign of the two youngsters at the rear. "Let's go around the front of the shed."

My sister follows.

"I'm going to go in the fenced-off area alone. You be lookout at the entrance and let me know if anyone comes."

My sister is on edge. That makes two of us.

We shouldn't really be on this part of the land—the farmer had been clear it would be trespassing. If he catches us, he might not let us feed the rest of the colony. We're risking everything, big time.

I duck down and creep along, winding in and out of the huge conifer trees. I grab the shed door handle and try to push it open, but it's locked. No surprise there. Do I break the door down? The farmer will know for sure we've been snooping around if I do. I know I'd better go and ask my sister for her opinion.

As I creep back towards her, I walk around the perimeter wall. It's been frosty and snowy on and off for a couple of months and I notice something that looks like orange-coloured fluff on the icy grass.

As I approach the small pile of fluffy fur, I notice it has the spine and skull of a cat. 'Sis!' I scream. It's Cassandra-Dior. It's her beautiful, long-haired calico coat. She is dead. My heart breaks.

"Are you okay?" She can't see me but runs towards the sound of my voice.

"One of the kittens is dead! Here."

My sister runs through the conifer trees towards me, no longer even pretending to care about being spotted. "Where?"

"There," I point in front of me.

"Are you sure?"

"Yes! Her bones are there and everything," I splutter as I begin to sob. Her fur was so long and beautiful that it still remained, covering the bones of the poor dead cat like a shroud.

"Where's Leo-Nigel?" she asks frantically.

"He might be here too. Let's look." I wipe the tears from my eyes.

We scan the ground for something, anything. . . and there he is. He is decomposing too, just like his sister. Both seemingly perished in the early winter months. We are heartbroken. Their lives were cut too short, and the worst thing is that their deaths could have been avoided.

Questions start to form in my mind. Why are their bodies so very close together? It's a horrible sight. We don't know why they died; there are so many possible reasons. Maybe they caught infections after their TNR; maybe Magdalena released them too early; maybe the horrible freezing winter weather got them, and they passed away from cat flu or pneumonia; maybe it was poison that killed them. This is the sad reality of a feral cat's life.

We don't have any shovels or boxes on us, so we decide to come back tomorrow and bury both of their little souls. We wish with all our hearts that we could have saved them. People often tell me how these feral cats would've been beautiful house cats. That's just it.

Would've.

Could've.

Should've.

Rest in peace, little boy and little girl.

CHAPTER FOUR

I know what I do for a living is a little naughty. I imagine many people would have something negative to say about it all, but I also dare to wonder whether people would respect what I do. Would they think it was wrong saving lives, even if by any means necessary? Who cares what anyone thinks about me, anyhow? It's a lucrative business to be in, because sex sells and is always a necessity in life that will never fade.

After Cassandra-Dior and Leo-Nigel died we were haunted by the sad fact that with record-breaking harsh winters predicted, we needed to rescue more feral cats, or they would die. That next winter my mother let me use her dining room to harbour the barn cats colony, and it saved their lives. I got them vaccinated, defleaed, dewormed, and had them given health MOTs, with any tooth extractions paid for. I had them microchipped too, and many had cat flu, so I had to have plenty of antibiotics to hand. I couldn't even get them all, so I dotted extra huts around outside with straw. Cat litter, cat food and cleaning products cost me a fortune but the look of realisation on their little faces as they saw they wouldn't have to struggle to survive was worth every penny. I could tell they were loving being cosy and warm indoors. And their little feet weren't frostbitten.

People worldwide had started to follow the feral cats I care for on social media, and I suddenly had contact from cat-lovers in America and as far away as the Philippines. I also got some donations of cat food, and although it wasn't enough for the cats to survive on alone, it was something.

I'm still wondering about the cat from the country lanes so I return. I head to the farm, two miles away from where I caught her. It's a desolate place. As soon as I enter their property, a young man speeds towards me on a quad bike, maybe trying to intimidate me. An older woman looks at me through the window and I get the impression she doesn't want me here. Fair enough. I am an intruder on their land. I wind the window down slightly. Anything could happen to me here. No one knows where I am, and everyone knows that farmers have guns. I smile nervously.

"Hi. I'm wondering if you could help me? I saved a cat a couple of miles down the lanes—she's black and white. I'm not sure if she belongs to you?"

"Have you got her in the back?"

"No. I took her to the vet. I'll show you a picture of her on my phone." He didn't wait to see the picture. I'd mentioned a vet, so he probably thought he'd be liable for the cost.

"Nope, she's not from here."

"Ah, no problem, thanks. I wonder where she came from, then? Do you have any other cats here?"

"Yes."

"Oh, how many?" I try to keep him talking.

"Quite a few." A man of few words, but I persist.

"I help cats. Do you need any help? I can neuter them, and I can help any that need vet care."

"Don't think we need help." I know farmers are set in their ways, and many who rear livestock to be sent to slaughter don't really care about any animals that can't fetch a decent price at the market. I see him look over at the woman, who's still watching. Maybe she's the boss; she has a hard look, and her eyes are angry.

"Do you have kittens here?"

He nods.

"Well, if they're breeding then I don't mind helping. Is there any way I can look at the kittens to see if they're okay? It's coming up to winter and they may be poorly?" He considers this for a moment and then leads me to a lambing shed. I enter through piles of slushy mud. I should have put my wellies on. The first thing I see is a dead kitten. Poor baby.

"Do you feed them?" I can't see any food or water.

"Sometimes in the winter we feed them, but not in the summer."

Wow. Seriously? What the actual fuck. This isn't the first time I've come across this mentality. I see a small, black, fluffy cat with patches of fur missing scarper. That's what feral cats do. She could be the mum—I bet that's her dead kitten. There are others—two fluffy black kittens and one tortoiseshell—all around two weeks old. The man picks one up. "You little dirty hisser." He plonks it back on the little bit of straw.

I was surprised to see the kitten hiss. You go, little one. No need to call it dirty.

"They're sneezing. They're going to die if you don't let me help." He shrugs.

"You'd have to ask my mum."

We head back to the front where there are about five sheepdogs and a few other terrier type dogs all barking at me. The dogs look well fed, and that's what I can't understand. If they can feed the dogs, then why not the cats?

"They're all starting to interbreed. They even chucked a Siamese out the other day, so something has to be done." Finally, he sees sense. But will his mum? "We have a couple of kittens inside. My girlfriend brought them in."

"And do you feed the ones inside?"

"Yes. Just not the ones outside, as they're semi-feral." I wish they understood that all animals need help, regardless of their status.

"I understand you want the cats to hunt and eat the rats, but they still need to eat, and will be better hunters if fed. That mum cat needs to eat five times more when she's pregnant."

"Oh. It looks like we're out of food, anyway." He points at a few empty mucky plastic bags of dry cat food. They look like they're from years ago. Ugh.

"These kittens won't make it out here. Would you let me take them? They need to see a vet."

He nods. I rush to the car to get an empty cat food box.

"I'll leave you to it" He walks off and leaves me head-to-head with his mum. She already has her arms folded and a face like thunder.

"Who are you?" she says sharply.

I smile, hoping to disarm her a bit. "I was just telling your son. I found a cat, but he said she's not from here. I've seen a few cats killed on the main road and I thought they must be yours."

"I can't help it if they get run over!" Her voice starts to rise, and I need to act quickly to keep her calm and on-side.

"Your son said cats are breeding here, and the kittens are poorly. Some are dead already."

She frowns. "I didn't know there were any kittens." Not a huge surprise, if she doesn't even care about the cats she has.

"I can help with neutering. I help cats." She shakes her head.

"I don't need your help. I don't know you. I'm funny about strangers." I totally get that. Why should she trust me? She's old school, and I probably couldn't break her mentality even if I tried. It'll have been ingrained in her by her parents. I reach round to the bag I have slung over my shoulders.

"Here's some cat food." She glares at me.

"No, I'll get some. I don't need charity." If looks could kill. "Look, I don't know you." She folds her arms again and I can tell from her body language that this conversation is over.

"Do please reconsider. I'll leave you my details. Have a look on my social media page at what I do, then you'll trust me. Take my number."

Whilst she gets a pen and paper, I nip out to the car and bring in a pile of cat-food boxes, regardless of whether she wants it or not. But will she feed the poor cats? Probably not, but I have to try.

On my way home, I stare at the open cat-food box and see the tiny kittens I'd managed to sneak away staring back at me. I did what I had to. Her son gave me the nod and she didn't have to know.

And I'm not done there yet.

CHAPTER FIVE

I'm in the orange, suede-themed bedroom two, on a weekend shift, when I first encounter someone who would become one of my addicted regulars. I nickname him the Ball Stroker after our first session. You'll find out why.

Phil is one of my favourite guys, as he spends mountains of money on me. He has paid for two of my sister's Intellectual Property Law books, three Equity & Trust Law books, two Human Rights Law books, one Sports Law book, two Criminal Justice Law books, and three Employment Law books, each costing about £40. My sister's university friend has been complaining to her about the law library only stocking four copies of the Intellectual Property Law book they need to help write their next essay. They've all been loaned out and, apparently, she's having to wait till the library gets them back in. Kitty could never admit that she actually owns a copy because the Ball Stroker bought my time and then I bought her the book.

Ball Stroker is about five feet ten inches, silver-tongued and well-mannered. He has thinning auburn hair and a pale face with glacial blue eyes. He calls his hair 'strawberry blonde'.

He's a few years older than me, has a medium physique with the cutest little pixie nose. I'm not, however, attracted to him sexually—this is strictly business.

The first time I meet him, Ball Stroker is showering as I walk in. I'm flaunting a cream, lace, see-through leotard, with matching cream, lace bra and French knickers underneath. I have my slender, polished legs on show and the leotard emphasises my curved, apple-shaped bum.

"Cat, is it?"

"Yes. Lovely to meet you." And I mean every word. I never know what to expect when first meeting a client. I have to ask specific questions, usually whilst they're relaxed and in receipt of a prick-teasing kiss or a sensual back massage. "So, what specialities do you like in the bedroom?" If they seem uneasy about this question then I speak again, gently, softly, to entice. "Have you visited here before?" I'm sure to receive a reply to this. If they reply "no," or "not for a long time," then I clue them up on what is on offer and the price list. . . because law books and cat food aren't cheap.

Ball Stroker is spaced out, as though something is on his mind. Eventually, I discover that he has suffered from depression most of his adult life. Coming in here is one way he can escape, I suppose.

"I've brought some things in with me," he says. "I'll show you." He stands up and fetches his black cotton rucksack. "I like to be teased and I don't have sex, but I inhale poppers. Is that okay with you?"

"That's fine by me." I am perfectly happy to be paid to keep my knickers on.

He perches on the king-sized orange bed with a peachy

towel wrapped around his half-dried body, and unpacks his rucksack, including a plastic pump bottle of olive oil, to spray intermittently on his balls. He brings poppers for his own use and a tub of Vaseline, which he rubs on his nostrils to prevent the poppers from burning his pixie nose.

He lies back on the mattress, with three pillows keeping his head upright, and removes the towel. Unlike most clients he isn't hard yet and I need to get to work on this soft matter. He places his essentials next to us as we make ourselves comfortable. I sit to his right, kneeling up with my body facing front-on towards his privates. He explains, as he spurts the oil on his balls, "If you can massage, tickle and stroke my balls while I inhale the poppers, it turns me on." He twists open his small, brown, glass bottle of poppers.

"You have the nicest bum I've seen in a long time," he says.

"Why, thank you, kind sir." I giggle and he chuckles.

I take off my shimmering gold stilettos, so I can get comfortable for this thirty-minute sitting, fondling his oily ball-sack as he inhales poppers every few minutes. I make him hard.

"Would you like me to moan while I'm teasing you?" Sex noises turn most guys on.

"No, carry on as you are, Cat."

Our time is almost over and he hasn't come. I've had him on the verge of an orgasm three times. Each time he tells me to stop, let him settle, then carry on teasing again.

"There's not long left."

"Oh, dear." He's quite posh. "Could I possibly engage you for another thirty minutes? I'll provide you with the booking fee and you can pay it to the receptionist. And I'll give you your mandatory fee now for the forthcoming time."

I'm aware that my next booking is waiting in the lobby area with his four cousins.

"I have another thirty-minute appointment now. I'm sorry. You're welcome to wait in the reception area for me and I promise I'll make it quick with this next guy for you."

While negotiating the sale I loop my hair around my fingers and maintain eye contact.

"Yes, great. Lovely. Lovely."

After each client we are told to straighten up the room, to make it look untouched. The next client walks through the hallway entrance into heaven (heaven being where the bedrooms are). He literally only lasts one-and-a-half-minutes, whilst I skilfully toss him off, but he seems content with my hand job and the build-up to me stripping off my lingerie, despite the fact he fluffed easily at my handiwork.

Ball Stroker is waiting for me on a leather sofa in the reception area. As I walk into the lobby changing room I can see him sipping a cup of coffee from behind the shutter doors.

Hours pass. In total, Ball Stroker has spent five thirty-minute services with me. Session one having given him the taste for my teasing talent, he booked three more slots. Then, as if one hundred and twenty minutes of me wasn't enough, he arrived back in the evening for his fifth and final tantalising session after he'd been home to feed his cat.

"I spend too much on punting, Cat," he admits. "But if I were to quit my addiction then half of the females in the county would be out of a job."

"Really? How hilarious." I doubt this very much, but I agree with him because he's paying. I've just remembered the tax on my car is up for renewal in five days.

"Last year I was treated for sex addiction and received counselling from a male counsellor," he tells me as I stroke his balls with my oily hand.

"Oh, right. Were you?" Obviously, the counselling hasn't worked.

"I think the problem is the poppers, Cat. They're the addictive thrill I seek. I'm wasting my family's savings doing this."

I learn that his family owns a company that manufactures art equipment, mainly rolls of art paper for schools. There's another branch of Palace Lounge and the factory is in between both parlours, so he's in easy commuting distance. I wonder if his family knows of his sex addiction. We all have our secrets.

Not all clients are so pleasant. As soon as I walk into the boudoir for my next appointment, the Scotsman is stepping out of the shower with his trivial erection on show. All five foot three of him. He smirks, as if he knows he'll adore what he has in store for me.

He drives my body up against the boudoir wall, brutishly rubbing his erection against me.

"Stand still," he demands aggressively.

I feel claustrophobic as he throws my body onto the bed and strips me naked, ripping down my balconette satin bra and yanking off my satin thongs. I pretend I'm excited by the force, even though I'm feeling a bit vulnerable.

He yanks my hair away from my neck so he can bang kisses on it.

He doesn't speak as I place the condom on him, he just drags me all over the mattress, plunging his pot belly on top of me: shit, his body is heavy. He holds me in missionary whilst he begins to sweat. Drip. Drip. Drip. He keeps me in this unmoveable position so he can control himself from finishing: method to his madness.

If I'd been riding him I'd have made him come within two minutes, but still he pumps himself into me, fast then slow, fast then slow. No talking, just his panting. The whole time I keep the session finishing time in my mind: six-thirty. Six-thirty. Saying the time over and over again in my mind. Six-thirty.

I'm becoming sore. I glance over at the digital clock on the stereo. It's four minutes until six-thirty. Finally. He only has four minutes to spurt and for us both to get showered, dressed, and out for my next client.

"You only have a few minutes left." My legs are aching because he has kept me squashed for twenty-five minutes and I'm drenched in his fucking sweat. His pinkish skin is now a corned-beef colour. My eyes begin to roll as I say for a second time, whilst patting him on the shoulder, "You only have a few more minutes left, you know."

"Okay! Aye." He pumps his average size into me about thirty more times then finally squirts into the end of the rubber. I hold the condom down on him and I throw it out of me. I'm furious. I know he's run me over the thirty minutes he initially paid for. He could've come about fifty times, but he kept stopping himself. Fucking annoying.

There's a loud knock on my chamber door, confirming he's run me over.

"Right, one minute!" I shout. "Can I have the money, please?"

He blatantly ignores me as he begins dressing himself. "I'm still horny for more."

"Money. Please."

"Hold on!" He drags my waist towards his, yanking down my balconette satin bra again and tugging at my left nipple, smirking into my upset eyes, whispering, "I am so horny."

I feel violated. He believes he has the right to pull my nipple hard. I'm going to catapult my heel at his head if he touches me again. There's another knock on my door. "You're going to get me the sack. Can I have the money you owe me?"

Reluctantly, he passes over the notes from his tightly clenched palm, grinning whilst keeping me close to his pot belly. I free myself from his grasp, storming out of the confining bedroom towards the reception area with my money.

"You've been with that punter for forty-eight minutes and your next booking is expecting you. You are now running late for all your other customers," the receptionist reminds me.

"He's still in room three, he doesn't want to leave. He made me wait by his side until he got dressed, all before he paid up. He tried to undress me again when his time was over, yanking my nipple."

"You should ask for the money upfront so you can leave the bedroom as soon as time is up."

Like a bad omen, Dreaded Scotsman reappears on my following shift. "Would you pay me now, please," I say to him, "because we've had a few young lads try and run off today without paying, so from now on I'm asking everyone for the money upfront."

"Yes. Aye. O'course."

I take my money and place it on the top shelf under my locker key, out of sight. Yet again, he fucks me in a trapped missionary position for the whole session, suffocating me with his weight, no talking, just panting, dripping sweat on me whilst stopping and starting, stopping and starting.

"You only have a few minutes left, where would you like to come?"

The bastard ignores me.

"Excuse me, but you are aware you only have a few more minutes left of your time. So, when the thirty minutes are up, I'll be leaving the bedroom."

He tells me to wank him off. I take off the condom and place lubricant on my hand. I start to toss him off. He's still stopping himself by carrying out breathing exercises.

"If you don't come within the next minute, I'll have to leave the room."

"Carry on!" he shouts at me aggressively.

I'm trying to help him finish off, because I don't want any of my clients leaving dissatisfied, putting bad reviews about me online, but this man is twofold taking the piss again.

"Your thirty minutes has ended and I'm getting dressed now."

I grab my lingerie and remuneration off the top shelf as he starts trashing the place. With my other hand I grip a towel around my body and escape from the bedroom, not even showering. Running to the lobby, I explain to the receptionist.

Twenty minutes later he casually walks into the lobby. I have already lost my next client who walked out because my room wasn't free.

"She gave me a rushed service. I want my money back."

Luckily, Angel is here to witness him lying, and both she and the receptionist already know of his previous piss-taking, so they defend me.

"You have taken fifty minutes in the room and your service has not, in fact, been rushed, but you have stolen an extra twenty minutes with Cat. If you wish to have more time with another girl, you can pay."

He shakes his head ferociously and then sits his arse down on the leather sofa, watching the area for the next ten minutes, letting his corned-beef face cool down.

After he leaves, the receptionist checks on her computer to see if any negative comments have been placed under his membership number and reads out what she finds.

"Known timewaster. Given four girls grief. Warning, very forceful with girls. Damaging property. Tried having sex more than once in the bedroom after his services had ended."

So, I'm not the only girl who has had to put up with his shenanigans.

I never have to deal with the Scotsman again. Fortunately, most clients are a lot more fun than that.

"Cat, is it okay if this client goes into your bedroom and Candy follows you? It's for a two girl," the receptionist asks me.

"That's fine, my bedroom's ready. Thanks."

The new client is a face I haven't seen before. He looks at me as though I'm fresh fruit. "I will surely see you in a minute, baby," he says, tapping me on my butt cheek.

I'm sporting apple-green French knickers, looking imposingly edible. If he's paying for an engaging threesome the chances are he's not short for cash.

"I love threesomes, me," Candy giggles.

"So do I. This is more exciting than a typical day job," I reply.

"You take the lead then, Cat. Get him to spend his cash, babe." Candy spurs me on, knowing I'm a good money-spinner.

"Definitely, honey. We'll see how much money he has." I wink at her as we finalise our make-up.

He's showering as we head towards the king-sized divan.

"Hola, sexy señoritas." He licks his top lip sexily, shower water rushing over his naked muscles.

"Hi, you." This sexy hunk seems to have stunned Candy. I can see it in her beautiful eyes. We exchange grins as he rubs his jet-black hair dry.

"Señoritas, it's my birthday today. I woke up this morning, having taken the day off work, and I thought, what better way to spend my birthday than having two beautiful señoritas please me."

"Why don't you get yourself comfortable on the bed?" I suggest.

"Ah, me gusta. Me gusta." He blows a kiss in the air at us both. He's one tease of a guy, but I'm attracted to it.

He's kneeling up between our bodies.

"I have plenty of money for each of you for the hour, so do as you please with my body, señoritas."

He has already placed the bulk of the money in the cabinet at the side of the divan.

"I've always wanted to play spin the bottle," I say. "How about we play it together?"

"Yes, sounds fun," Candy says.

"We can use my strawberry lube bottle. Whoever the lid lands on has to take on a dare I choose."

"I like the sound of this." He says, stroking my outer thigh lightly.

I whirl the strawberry lube in a clockwise motion on the silk bed sheet; it comes to a halt, the lid pointing at Candy.

"Candy," I say, "why don't you kiss him?"

"My pleasure." This live porno is making me moist.

When Candy spins, it ends up pointing at him.

"I want you," Candy tells him, "to take off Cat's bra."

He does as he's told and then takes his turn spinning the lubricant, peering at my revealed breasts. It stops at Candy.

"I want you, Candy, to kiss Cat, for me."

"I've always wanted to do that," she says. As we kiss she moans in enjoyment.

Our client has a noticeable hard-on.

"Wow, you're big and hard," Candy murmurs.

"My turn," I say. I want to be the one in charge. "I want you to slide down Candy's knickers and whip off her bra."

Candy allows him to slowly strip her.

"I want Cat to spin the bottle again, using my turn," Candy wants me in control as well.

"Yes, I like giving the orders. It turns me on." We all laugh.

"Oh, it's landed on you again, handsome," Candy says.

"What would you like me to do, Miss Cat?" He reaches for my breast and strokes it.

"Candy and I would like you to tug on yourself. Isn't that right, Candy?"

"Yes, we absolutely would. Wank it for us." Her eyes twinkle.

"Come here. I'll put some of this lube on you." I rub it slowly, delicately.

"Okay, my beautiful señoritas. I will play with my manhood for you both."

"Oh, yes, make us both wet. It turns me on. Keep tossing it."

"Can I fuck one of you? My body is telling me it's ready for one of your soft pussies."

"I want to see you fuck Candy."

"Cat, will you talk dirty to me while I fuck Candy?"

"You want me to talk dirty in your ear while you bend Candy over and pound her?"

"Yeah, baby, yeah, señorita."

"Bend her naked body over. Now, let me place this condom on you," I get him ready to give it to her. "Candy are you ready for him inside you? Tell us you're ready."

"Yes, Cat, I'm ready."

"Do you want him to push it into you, thrusting you slow? Sexing deep, nice and deep?"

"Yes, Cat. Yes, I do." Candy is bent over.

But the client hesitates. "Girls, I saw a position in a Kama Sutra book. It's called the churning of the cream. It's where one of you lays on your back and I lift your bum up, pushing your knees next to the sides of your face. I squat above you, holding your thighs down as I stand over you."

"Sounds fun," Candy says.

"I will go nice and deep for you." He knows what she wants.

I tap her bum cheeks as she lays on her back for him, spreading her legs slightly.

"I know you love me spreading her open for you," I say.

"Yeah, I fucking love this." He's in his element.

"We want you to bang us both hard in our slutty fannies," I give him more dirty talk.

"You do, do you? Yeah, I want to do some hard fucking today, ladies."

"Oh, yes," Candy moans in satisfaction.

"She loves you, darling. She loves it sliding deep inside her. Go on darling, fucking give it to Candy, make her scream for you. Do as I say!"

"You need me to fuck you, baby?" He's squatting downwards, thrusting into her.

"She needs you. Keep giving it to her. Fuck her, make her moan loud."

"Shit! Yes! I love this big one." Candy really does seem to love it.

"I will fucking come if you two dirty señoritas carry on speaking filthy like this to me."

"Are we turning you on, baby?" Candy asks, still with her bottom held up high.

"Yeah, you are." He spanks our bottoms hard.

"When you're about to finish, why don't you pull out of Candy and finish all over both of our lips?"

"Yeah, I want to spunk on your beautiful faces. Both of your beautiful faces," he yelps. "Oh, fucking hell!" He's banging Candy faster from above, sliding downwards faster and faster. "I'm about to explode, señoritas. Fucking shit!"

"Let me wank you on my face then, darling," I trail my nails on his arm.

He slides out of Candy and whips off the rubber. "Where should I aim, baby?"

"Spunk on my face." I kneel, while he stands above me, sturdy on my divan. "Come here and sit next to me, Candy. Let him wank onto our faces."

Candy joins in, wanting him all over her.

"Oh, fucking hell. I'm going to fucking come on your

beautiful faces, all over your beautiful lips." He's looking as though he's trying to water his front garden with a large hosepipe.

"Do it! Do it now, you dirty bastard," Candy is getting pushy.

"Yes, darling. We want to see your spunk," I await his aim.

"It's coming. Are you two ladies ready?"

"Yes, baby, we want it now. Give it to us. Give us your juice."

He explodes, and it dribbles over our lips and chins.

"How about that, señoritas?" He's awestruck with himself. "Best birthday ever. Thank you."

"Yeah. You burst, you did," Candy wipes her face with a tissue. She passes me some tissues to wipe my chin.

We've had fun with this one.

"I'll be coming back to see you again, Cat. I will fuck you soon."

"I'll be waiting." I cup my bra-covered breasts flirtatiously as he leaves.

CHAPTER SIX

"Hi! Can I book an appointment for Beauty and Cinderella, please? They had their consultations yesterday. Beauty needs an enucleation [eye removal] and Cinderella needs dental work."

I'd decided to use a different vet practice this time after the last one tried to convince me to put Beauty to sleep due to her left eye being ruptured and the loss of most of her vision in her other eye.

"Someone's a fan of book charachters, then?" the receptionist asks, chuckling down the phone.

"What do you mean?"

"You know, Cinderella, and Beauty."

I smile. "Oh yes, sorry! We have an Alice, too. And Pocahontas." When we first began to feed them, we couldn't keep track of who was who. "I just saw that black and white one," I'd point.

"Which black and white one? There's loads of black and white ones." My sister would scan the area with her eyes.

"You know, that long-haired one."

"There's probably about ten long-haired ones." How could we keep track of them all without them giving them names?

Beauty. To me she's so very beautiful. Beauty is the one that gave birth to the kittens in that nettle bush and then ran off because she was scared. She keeps her long black and white fur pristine. One of her eyes is clouded, and the other looks as if it's sunken in her head or ruptured. If I'm honest, I was shocked when I first saw her eyes. I felt it was such a damn shame for her and I really didn't know how she navigated. They say cats are clever and they use their whiskers, so they don't bang into things, and other senses too, such as hearing and smell. I always wonder if she'd been attacked or whether it's hereditary, like the other kitten with a ruptured eye we had to surrender to the vets.

Pocahontas is a calico girl. She has long, silky fur and she's the daughter of Petal. When I was younger my nickname was Pocahontas, too, because of my long, dark hair. She's only a young girl but she's independent. Pocahontas the cat does what she wants—that includes smacking me if I make one wrong move, but she also has a loving side and allowed me to stroke her a couple of times at the feeding station. I nickname her Pokie. One day I'd love to save her forever.

Alice is the eldest cat in the colony, although it's no magical wonderland for her—living outside is all she has ever known. She's like the grandma cat and she's well respected by the rest of the colony, not afraid to tell them what for even though she's an older lady. I just felt like Alice suited her. She doesn't fare well outside though, sneezing. I always prayed she'd pull through. I don't have to worry about her now as I brought her in and she's cosy, warm and fed.

Cinderella. I nickname her Rella. Maybe one day I can be her Fairy Godmother—there for her when she needs me most.

*

"All clear," I say, as I clamber out of our mother's car. She's dropping me off at work as a favour. I clutch my luggage containing condoms, lube, dildos, nurses' outfits and handcuffs, and run precipitously over the white gravel to the red back door.

I spot Angel. "Hurry," Angel whispers, and we both let out squeals of joyous laughter as we run, like kids.

We're always anxious about who might be lurking outside. We know some clients are hooked on us and if they got the chance in the 'real world', they'd try to talk to us, date us or maybe something worse.

"Let us in," I stab at the buzzer beside the camera. The bulky red door instantly unlocks. I push open the door. I feel as though one day I want to be opening a door like this at a place of my own, being the boss. I won't be wearing stockings and suspenders. The boss lady here wears nothing less than a suit. She's a force to be reckoned with. I look up to her. I want to become a boss lady like she is. She only cares about how well her business is run, how she can have the best staff to make it as profitable as possible. She's not afraid to sack on the spot—I've seen it first-hand. I'm one of her favourites though. I don't mess about. I get my head down—literally. And I make every customer feel as though he's having the dream experience of his life so he will return, be it weekly or fortnightly. I get them hooked. The boss tells me she was like me in her younger years. She worked here when she first started out and she had some amazing reviews.

"Let me tell you, Cat. I used to tie them up and leave them, and that's why they came back. Because I was in charge," she once told me.

Nobody ever messed with her, and they still don't.

Angel and I step in and wait for the internal door to open. The heavy red door closes behind us and locks.

"Hello, girls," the receptionist and cleaner greet us with tired morning smiles.

Our first responsibility is to examine our booking sheets for the day ahead. We both need to know who we are seeing, for how long and how many reservations we have. I am fully booked from ten-thirty. I know I'll be going home with a full purse today.

Most of the names on the sheet are familiar, some not. Zane: I haven't met him before. Stevie: he owns a canal boat. Sam: he has a little pet pig in his house and his wife's just given birth to triplets. Adam: likes to finger me loads, wasting time, because he knows he finishes off too soon. Alonzo: a chef who tells me he'll cook for me one day. Kendrick: has the biggest dick I've ever seen. Max: has twin girls and never has sex with his wife—so he says. Ali: always says he wants a threesome (even suggests getting my sister involved). But there's not just one Ali I see, and anyway, it could be an Ali I've never met before. If it's *the* Ali I think it is, he can keep dreaming—a threesome with my sister is never going to happen, for anyone. She doesn't do what I do. Shamrock: Irish. Bobby: I see a few blokes named Bobby, not sure which one this is. Yingjie: new. Vincent: a high school teacher. Xavier: a stranger to me—but I quite like fucking strangers. Rak: likes to fuck me about ten times, one after the other; I've never known a guy fuck so much in one go! He drives two hours to see me and prefers

84

to see me for two and a half hours in one booking. However, it seems he's just snuck in for thirty minutes at eight-thirty tonight and usually in that time a client's only allowed to fuck once. Maybe he can do it two or three times if he pays extra.

I walk into the changing room and say to Angel, "I got in a pickle when you were upstairs in a booking. I saw a lad I went to high school with in the lobby, and he only tried to book me!"

"No, way! Honestly? Did you service him?"

"As if!" We both laugh.

"How did you get out of it then?"

"I had to wait till he went in my room before I could collar the receptionist and tell her there was no way I was seeing him. Then the receptionist told the cleaner to tell him I knew him and had obviously refused him."

"Was he okay with that?"

"Apparently he begged her to beg me."

"Ugh." Angel shakes her head. "What is wrong with some people?"

"Did you hear that Wonderful House was shut down last week?" Another girl brushes her hair in the mirror.

"Yes, one of my clients told me," I say.

"The boss has already interviewed loads of the girls who used to work there. They all want jobs here."

"That's the last thing we need. More competition," another girl butts in. I forget her name—there's around fifty girls who grind here.

"I heard she has employed ten of them already."

The parlour's website has more hits than any other masseuse website in England, or so I've been told. It reveals all the stats and specialities of each lady, photos included. I mean, everyone has a type they go for, right? And then there are the reviews.

'Cat is dazzling. Oral to completion. I'll be dreaming of my knob in her mouth forever. Her toned, tanned arse isn't one to forget. Cut above the rest, I say. I'll be returning.'

*

I never got that phone call off the farmer woman, and I'm not sure why I expect it, to be honest. The three kittens are doing well. One of them has sticky eyes, so thank goodness I took them. The farm has around one hundred and twenty acres of land—it's huge. It might be a big hunting ground for cats, but what if a cat isn't on form, through illness or old age? Does that mean they are just left to die out in the wilderness, and not be nursed back to health or fed? In this situation, I'm afraid the answer is usually yes—unless I can help. I pass by again, and see mummy cat in the fields, and it breaks my heart. What if she can't catch any food?

My sister and I head back to the desolate farm.

"Hi. I was just wondering if it would be okay to see if I can catch mum cat and have her spayed? She could also be suffering from mastitis, as her kittens have been taken away."

"She will also need antibiotics, as her kittens have cat flu," my sister butts in. I thought I'd try a different approach this time, so I brought backup. I even brought a big bag of dog food as a goodwill gesture to get them on side. Luckily, the woman who was so nasty the last time is nowhere to be seen.

"Erm, yeah, if you want. Owt for nowt."

"We can bring her back after she's done."

"That's if you want her back," chimes in Kitty. "Do you?"

"Yeah. We've made the mistake before of letting another cat charity take a pregnant cat a while ago, and they didn't bring her back." No surprise there. Doesn't he wonder why? I'm very happy to explain it to him—because they're starving to death and anyone with a heart recognises the neglect. It's hard enough for the poor cats living outside as it is.

Pretty much straightaway, a tiny black kitten with a brown face is showing interest in the trap. I'd say this one is only twelve weeks old at the most. Once we have her safely captive, the mother doesn't want anything to do with the trap. The young farmer approaches us. I think he wants us to leave.

"Can we come back and trap mum cat?"

"Yeah. Just bring the cats back, though, once they're done."

Can I honestly promise him this? No. In my opinion, he doesn't deserve to have any cats here. I wonder how they treat the sheep and cows. The dogs look well fed. Sheepdogs live outside, and other dogs live inside. Again, what's the difference between the working sheepdogs and the house dogs, just like the outdoor cats and the indoor cats? I can't tell.

They say once you bring a feral kitten in, time is of the essence. As each day passes, they become more feral, which to me is just another word for nervous. I recall the young farmer saying the black kitten was extremely feral and although kittens are only small, believe me when I say their pin teeth hurt when they sink into your hand, so I'm not chancing it. I get my funny-looking gauntlets on—they're like something a clown would wear, bright red and yellow gloves. They extend all the way up my arm. Usually, kittens at this age hiss, spit and growl.

As I get closer, it starts to panic and runs around the hospital basket looking for an escape route, backing as tightly as it can into the corner. The poor thing is frightened to death.

"Hey, it's okay," I say in a soft voice. "Everything's going to be okay. You're safe now. I won't hurt you." I close my eyes and rub the kittens chin and in return it closes its eyes, which is a sign of trust in cat body language. No need for these gauntlets; they're so bulky, and it's hard to stroke a cat properly wearing them.

"You're so beautiful. I think I'll name you Blossom. You can't live outside like that, can you?" I tickle her ears and cheeks and want to pick her up and just cradle her. "Aww, don't be scared. You'll be nice and warm tonight, Blossom, and now you won't ever be hungry again."

CHAPTER SEVEN

Now that people can see how much I am helping cats in need they often contact me, asking for advice.

"I've been feeding a cat in my back garden for about two weeks. It looks really dirty. I think it's lost. I'm not sure if it's neutered. It looks like he still has balls. I'm not sure what to do. Can you help?"

So, first things first: paper collar the cat.

If you can get close enough, place a paper strip around the cat's neck and sticky-tape it on the ends. If it has an owner, then you can write your contact details on the paper collar and the owner should come forward. Mystery solved! Paper-collar templates can be found on the internet and can be printed off—or you can even make your own.

If you can pick up the cat, place it in a cat carrier and take it to a local vet. Tell them your situation and get them to check the cat for a microchip. It may have an owner who is looking for it, and vets have access to the microchip website and ownership details which the general public don't.

But if you can't get close enough to the cat to place a paper collar round its neck, you'll need to contact a local cat organisation who might humanely trap it and scan for a microchip. Annoyingly, not all cats are microchipped.

If the cat is not microchipped and found injured, for example if it's been hit by a car, vets are allowed to put them to sleep. Some cat organisations will fight for the cat's life, but others don't. If the cat isn't microchipped then nobody can foot the vet's bill, and if they think the cat is feral, they will most likely put it to sleep because not many can home a feral.

If you come across a cat that you're worried about, it's worth taking a picture of it and putting it on Lost and Found websites in and around the area. Check through the website's pictures and descriptions to see if the cat is already listed as missing. If it is, you should be able to contact the owners from there.

Don't assume a wandering cat is missing from home, because cats roam for many reasons. Males may roam for a female if they aren't neutered. Cats like to be around other cats, and they also move around in search of a variety of food. At the same time, though, do be open to helping them, as it may indeed be lost, and if it is, it will need food and water.

*

At work, as I'm taking a bite to eat before my next booking arrives, Paris comes in after seeing out a client. "I hate that guy. He comes to see me every week. He stinks. Sometimes I wish I didn't have to do this job."

"I can't believe you travel all the way from Newcastle every week."

"It's horrible where I live. You'd hate it. It's a rough council estate. Cars get set on fire there all the time."

"Do your parents know what you do?"

"I shit meself a few months ago. Me dad saw I'd been looking at work's website on our house computer. Me mam told me he'd told her about it. Me mam blamed it on me brother. Me mam knows I work here. Me dad thinks I'm a stripper in London."

"My mum knows I work here too. She says she'd do it, if she had her time again. Why did you tell your dad you're a stripper?"

"I didn't want him wondering how I got me new sports car, breast implants, designer watch, hair extensions, designer handbags, designer clothes. I didn't want him asking where I was going two days a week. I help me mam and dad pay their bills. Me elder sister used to be a prossie when she was younger, that's how I found out about the wage."

"Do your friends in Newcastle know what you do?"

"Nah, I don't tell anyone. Some girls in me area chat shit about me though."

"They're jealous of you, I bet."

"I work part-time in a clothes shop too so they can't prove shit. Don't stop them chatting though."

"They probably need some gossip because their lives are boring," I say.

I guess we all need to keep some normality in our lives; Paris working in a clothes shop part-time, me helping cats in need.

Sunshine is in the changing room, too. The one who serviced an A-list celebrity when she was an escort, before starting here. Her website says she's in her mid-twenties but that's a fib; she's thirty-eight and has a twenty-something-year-old son. She's half-Jamaican and her father is from the

Netherlands, so she tells everyone she's part Dutch, but she can't speak a word of the language.

"Does your mum know you work here, Sunshine?" I ask.

"Yeah, she knows I'm a brass. My mother walked out on my brother, my sisters and me when we were kids. I only remember my gran bringing me up. My mum left my dad for a woman. I work here to bring my son up. I had him when I was young, you see. Didn't want him having the life I've had. No money. No nice clothes. No car. No mother."

"Do you see anything of your mum now?"

"Yeah, now I do. I don't resent her for leaving my dad. If she's a lesbian, fuck it, I say."

"She's lucky to have a daughter like you who understands," I say.

"I remember visiting my mum when I was a little girl, and if my gran came into my mum's house then my mum's lesbian lover would run upstairs and hide under my mum's bed. When my gran left, I'd run upstairs and shout, 'It's okay now, Aunty Jackie, you can come out from under the bed!' How fucking funny now I know Aunty Jackie was my mum's bird."

"Why did your mum's girlfriend hide from your grandmother?"

"My gran would've been ashamed to think my mum enjoyed women licking her out," Sunshine chuckles. "My mum had to live a lie for years in fear the family might disown her. That's why I don't tell anyone I work here. Only my mum and sisters know. My family would fuck me off. Not even my son knows."

"We all have skeletons in the closet. I don't tell any friends or family, but my mum and sister know."

"Don't blame you," Paris says.

"What do you tell your other family and friends you work as then?" I don't know how Sunshine explains to her family how she can afford fake tits—size double F cups—liposuction, lip implants, new dentures, or buying her house and car outright.

"I just tell them I do hair extensions. I can do weaves and put hair extensions in, so they believe me. Sometimes I do weaves for a few girls. I'd like to buy my own hairdressing salon one day. Rent a room out to someone so they can do nails or tanning. That's my dream. . . Hiya, love." Sunshine welcomes a stroll-in gent.

My booking, Carl, arrives behind him. I've seen him for the past six weeks running. Once a week he comes here for a good time. Simple service. Bit of a blow job, then sex with me on top until he finishes.

Sunshine doesn't know that I know she also works for a renowned escort company, as well as being on another escort website, which isn't allowed by the boss. No girl who works at the parlour is permitted to work elsewhere within the same region. Sunshine hides her identity well, though, wearing a brunette wig over her copper-coloured, curly weave. Wish I could do the same. I just don't have any spare time what with rescuing all the cats.

At least we all have our mothers to confide in. Having a strong mother-daughter relationship has helped me massively in life. My mother has always been there to guide me through difficult situations, any time I've felt unsure on how to go about things, she always has a shoulder I can lean on, and with her life experiences she's wise, and above all non-judgemental. And we can talk to each other. Being able to talk to someone makes me feel less isolated. We are all living double lives, in a sense, and it's not always easy. But I think we women are a lot stronger, both mentally and physically, than we appear or even believe ourselves.

CHAPTER EIGHT

'What's my name?' The client is quizzing me, needing to know I have remembered him. Out of the hundreds of men I strip for and ride, how am I supposed to remember his name? He seems to be wearing a lot of purple. I try to remember if I've previously given him a nickname.

"Err, sorry. . . I've forgotten. It's been a few weeks, mind." I hug him.

"Kian."

"Yes, Kian—I remember now. I know exactly who you are. How could I possibly forget, you brought me the perfume last time?" I notice his gold wedding ring.

"Don't forget next time, Cat." Sanctioning me with his eyes, sullen at my poor memory. "Purple is my favourite punting colour."

"You don't say. I love the colour purple. As it goes, purple is a cat lady colour."

"I'm superstitious; purple has to be part of my outfit for the day, when I'm expecting to pay a visit. I always have a good punt when I wear it." He begins to untie his purple tie.

"Darling, you'll never have a bad punt with me." I pull his

purple pocket-handkerchief out of his shirt and throw it on the bed, biting my lower lip.

"That's exactly why I'm back for more."

"Is that so?" I kiss his lips and pull back.

"I'm becoming one of your regulars." He twists his purple cufflinks off, one after the other.

"Can't be a bad thing." I touch his crotch and he hardens instantly.

"I'll make it worth your while if you see me outside of here?"

"You know that's against the rules, darling." I slowly unbutton his shirt whilst looking into his grey eyes.

"Nobody has to know." He drops his suit pants to the floor, revealing his purple boxer shorts.

I drop to my knees and dip my hands into his boxers; his stiffness makes my mouth water. I know he'll feel amazing inside me. He firmly presses his thumbs on my temple and his fingers on my scalp, then massages my head whilst pushing himself into my mouth. I suck to the pace he controls and then he pulls back.

"I'll have to think about it," I say.

"Yes, you do that." He deepens into my throat.

I dig my nails into his butt cheeks and tighten my mouth around him, while my sucking gets faster.

"Enough of that for now. Fuck. You're going to make me explode."

Even though I'd forgotten his name, I remember him telling me he is a multi-millionaire, and he's in the aviation industry. On his first visit, he handed me a gift before the service. I knew from then on that this meant he wanted me to treat him as extra special.

I stand, and he begins to strip me naked, dropping my bra straps off both my shoulders at the same time, then unclasping my bra as he pushes his tongue deep into my mouth. My knickers drop to the floor and I'm stood in just my stockings and stilettos.

"Legs wide apart," he whispers, massaging my sex.

"Sure." I start to get wet.

He walks me to the mirrored wall.

"This is why I pay for you—to see and feel this body of yours." He raises his head to glance at us and runs his hands up to my breasts, squeezing them slightly. I can feel his stiffness pushing into the crease of my butt cheeks.

My hands push firmly against the mirror. "Kian, I need you inside me." I reach for the condom and place it on him. He stands naked behind me, bar his purple socks, and thrusts into me, slowly, then harder, my hips rocking backward and forward. He holds my breasts, tickling my nipples, then massages my sex again.

I turn around to face him, my eyes on his, "Harder. Give it to me. Show me what you're made of."

He slaps me lightly. "Can you take it all?"

Of course, I can. The harder the better. Yes, I still get turned on with clients. I use them for as much satisfaction as I can. Why not? Why can't a girl have a few orgasms a day? Kian's a gentle silver fox, he knows what gets him off, and he also knows how to please a lady.

"I can only finish when you tell me I've paid you for sex."

"This is what you want, isn't it, Kian? You pay me for this. You pay me for sex."

And he was right—magic words unleashed, and he has

finished. I could've made him finish much sooner by reminding him why he pays me, but that's the thing—I like to satisfy my clients and be satiated, so they come back for more.

"How about a massage?" I can't let him out the door yet, the receptionist will wonder why I've booted him out before the hour's up.

"Yes, please."

"Talc? Lotion? Oil?"

"Talc, please. Oil will stain my suit."

"Right you are."

"Give me another kiss."

My tongue swirls in his mouth for a few seconds. "You're going to get hard again."

"I need a full day with you."

"Maybe one day we will. Turn over." I shake the talc over his back. I had to change the subject, not that I don't want more of his thrusting, but he will run me over if we go at it again, and I need the money from the next client.

"Listen, I'm coming back to see you very soon," he says at the end, brushing his fingers through my hair and over my shoulders.

"Something for me to look forward to." I raise an eyebrow.

"That is if you remember my name," he shakes me by the arms, jokingly.

"I will. I will."

"Sure about that?" He reaches out for his clothes to re-dress.

"Positive." I must convince him because, let's face it, he's a good fuck.

"If you ever think of disappearing from here, please tell me before you do."

"I won't be leaving any time soon. I love it here."

"I'll give you my number."

"Don't worry, I'm going nowhere." Can I be totally sure of that? Who knows what's around the corner?

"Good. I will definitely be back soon, Cat." He kisses my neck three times, then knots his purple tie.

A few weeks later Kian returns, wearing purple again. And again, he brings me a present. This time it's a pair of silver tweezers with a mirror and a light, which—not surprisingly—can be purchased on airlines. I doubt many could say they get gifts alongside orgasms in their normal day job.

He eases my legs apart and strokes my sex with his tongue. His licks are warm.

I grip his head with my hands and push his head deeper into my sex. "Don't stop."

His hands trace up my body and he plays with my nipples simultaneously.

I look into his eyes and lick my lips, sucking on one of my fingers. I was once told by Victoria—another sex worker—to make plenty of eye contact with clients.

"Your tongue is amazing, Kian." My breathing becoming louder and faster.

"Do it. Come for me." I hear sex noises coming from the other rooms amidst the sensual music playing and I just know he'll love these moans and groans too. His tongue is sending shivers through my body and I widen my legs further. I look up at the ceiling and I can't deny it turns me on something wicked to see him beneath my legs. I look back down as his tongue is licking me incessantly.

"Fuck. Fuck." I moan as he pushes his finger inside me,

and then another. I'm getting wetter, and he forces another finger inside me. This feels too good to be true. "Harder, finger me harder."

I grip the bedsheet and close my eyes. I want him to fuck me so much.

"Kian, that's going to make me. . ." An orgasm floods my body.

"You remembered my name."

"How could I not?" I wink and take a deep breath and exhale. Fuck. Me. That was immense.

A week later, he's back again. "I've brought you something special."

"Thank you so much. You're lovely to me, Kian," I say, proving that I still remember his name. Well, truthfully, I had to check on the booking sheet before I entered the boudoir.

"Your present is on the bed, and so is your money, beautiful."

I remember he takes pleasure in paying a prostitute.

"Oh, so you've paid me now. I'll count it. You like paying me, don't you?" I smile cheekily. I open the gift bag to peek at what he's got me. A set of treatments for the face, hands, feet, body and legs. What a treat. The only treats I usually buy are cat treats. A day out shopping for me is a day in the pet shop, but if the cats are happy, I am too.

Placing my gift on the bedside table, I notice a pair of latex gloves on the mattress. I'm sure they weren't there before. Why would he place latex gloves on the bed?

He sprawls on the bed, naked after showering, picks the latex gloves up and flings them on the side. "They may be of use later on."

Whilst he was between my legs last time, he was begging

me for my real name. I didn't want to disappoint him because he brings me gifts, so I told him a name I wouldn't forget if he ever tested me. Ebony was the name I gave, my previous escorting name. I want to keep my identity hidden until I open my own brothel. Once I'm there, they can talk about me all they want. Sex sells and I've always been business minded. I've been looking at places to rent online and working out how much it'd cost me. The owners here must be raking it in with all the punters they get. If there are seven rooms and eleven hours in a day for seven girls, and if in every half an hour the booking-in fee is handed in at the desk, I'd be rolling it in. I'd never have to work again.

"Ebony, Ebony. . . oh, Ebony."

"Oh, you remembered. You have a fantastic memory. You like paying me, don't you?" I remind him. Secret weapon unleashed—he explodes—job done. We didn't use the latex gloves after all.

"I'm so glad you told me your real name," he says as he enters the shower. "Ebony really suits you."

Does this man seriously think I'm going to tell any client my 'real world' name?

"You aren't the only girl here who's told me her real name. Claire told me her real name, too."

"Really? What's her real name then?"

"Claire's real name is Fiona." He waits for my expression to reveal whether she's told him the truth.

Oh, my word! Claire really told him.

"Yes, that's her real name."

"See, she trusts me, and I'm happy you do too. Rose told me her real name, too. It's actually Kate. And Liberty's real name is Melissa. Don't say anything to them, but I put Claire's real name on one of the punter forums by mistake. It just slipped out."

*

I hear a loud and clear whisper: my name. I almost jump out of my skin thinking someone is behind me in my garden. If there were someone here it'd be a stranger, as I'm not expecting anyone. I glance around and Baby Girl—a semi-feral I rescued from the homeless barn cats—is on the window ledge, looking at me. She's squeezed through the gap in the window, and even though it seems a ridiculous thought, she is the only one who could've said it. I ring my auntie.

"You might not believe me but something really freaky happened. I'm sure my cat spoke to me."

"She's your familiar. Witches have cats, and cats have powers, too. She will make your powers stronger."

My auntie has always known about witchcraft. My mum has always called her abilities a 'gift'. When she was younger, she'd tell her siblings, "I am the witch with the big black hat," to keep them quiet and get them to sleep. All three of them have been live on TV doing psychic readings on shows.

I only got Baby Girl from the barn cats colony because she and her sister, Angelique, had cat flu. It was only meant to be temporary. As soon as I brought her in she was really nervous, climbing doors, I'd never seen a cat so agile. It was sad, but Baby didn't take well to the change of environment, and she hid for three weeks under the bed in the bedroom where it was quiet. Hunger got the better of her though, and over the weeks I managed to coax her out more and more for food. She watched her sister allow me to stroke her, and then something clicked—all of a sudden Baby rubbed up my back and let me stroke her. As time went on, we became closer and closer, to the point where I couldn't even go for a wee without her racing in to jump on my knee and invade my privacy. All around the house she followed me. So sweet. Baby and her sister loved the carpet so much, they kept rolling around and padding at it with their little paws. Such a beautiful sight. I was fascinated and kept videoing them. I'd always had dogs before and didn't know cats loved to play with strings and lasers and toy mice. But now Baby Girl was part of the family.

Baby Girl isn't the only familiar in the family. When Midnight, a fully black kitty, was left all alone in my local pet shop, other customers having taken all her siblings, my heart went out to her. I told my mum about her.

"I feel really sorry for this little black kitten in the pet shop. She's just in a cage next to the rabbits looking really depressed. Can we have her?"

"No," my mum said. "She'll be okay. Someone will take her."

"She's been there for weeks, and no one has yet. The guy in the pet shop said it's hard to home her as she's black and fluffy."

"Sorry, love."

"Midnight is a black cat. She will be your familiar and your powers will grow."

"No!" She was washing her hair in the bathroom and we were shouting from room to room.

"Doesn't every witch have to have a black cat?" I protest.

I hear my mother sigh, loudly. "Go on then. Go and get her."

To me, Midnight was extra special. I had to get her. She's been in our family ever since.

*

I'm so glad I didn't confide in Kian. To be honest, it could have been Kian's big mouth that caused Claire's boxer boyfriend to turn up kicking off, forcing Claire to take time off work. He barged through the door, in a violent rage, looking for her picture on the wall, screaming, "Where is she? Fiona, or Claire, as she calls herself? My missus, my baby's mum. She's a brass. When I find her, I'm going to fucking smash her in. Seriously, I'm going to smash the living day lights out of her. The fucking slut!"

Claire had phoned ahead, which gave the receptionist enough time to remove Claire's half-naked picture from the gallery wall and when he arrived, she acted puzzled.

"We don't have a Claire here. We have a Cassie, but no Claire."

"Don't fucking lie to me. You're all in on it. I've been told. She's been seen here. Seen by my mate. I'm no fucking idiot."

The receptionist remained silent as he marched up and down the gallery. Everyone knew he was a boxer, so nobody dared confront him. Claire had told stories of him serving sentences in prison for beating her up before. Now it probably made sense to him how she had bought her brand-new top-of-the-range sports car and her detached house, how she afforded all the jewellery sprinkled on her body and her designer handbags. Claire must be a decent liar because she's been in a relationship with him for years whilst being on the game and giving birth to their child. One has to either be a professional prevaricator to play the game or have a very dumb boyfriend.

Claire quit work after that. I wonder if he'll ever get proof, or if they'll rekindle their relationship. A source said Claire wouldn't be coming back as her boyfriend agreed to provide for her financially. I doubt very much he'd be able to carry her at the level she's used to. She's one of the busiest girls in the parlour, like me. She plays her game with clients exceedingly well. She knows how to get what she wants.

"I find out if clients are rich, what they do for a living, then home in on it," she explained to me. I doubt she'd give up selling herself so easily. Once a person finds out how to get plenty of money, it's hard to give up. I'm not leaving any time soon either.

*

Interesting travel bag under our bed! Lube, condoms, poppers, underwear, stockings, high heels and vibrators. We need to fucking talk. Right now!

Angel's fiancé has messaged. The man she's about to marry and spend the rest of her life with has discovered her workbag. Many unanswered questions must have crossed his mind. Thoughts such as: Is she cheating? What's she hiding? What's the cherry dick lick for?

Angel was quick to answer:

Cat used it when she went away for a naughty weekend with her boyfriend. I picked her up from the train station and she accidentally left her travel bag in the boot of my car. I haven't seen her for a while, so I decided to put it under our bed for now, until I see her again. x

Okay. X

He replied, 'Okay'! That's all? Desperate to keep her, it seems.

Is it possible for a girl to have this job and a boyfriend at the same time? After what I saw happen to Claire, I've warned Angel she's treading on thin ice. Her fiancé has his suspicions, as of now. Angel told me if she invited me to her wedding, I could blow her cover without intending to, so I wasn't invited. I didn't blame her. If I were to get married, I couldn't invite any call-girls to my wedding either because I'm sure my groom would wonder where my high-maintenance, false-titted, limp-implanted, teeth-veneered friends had all met.

"I told him I'd call the wedding off if he has no trust in me," she tells me. "How dare he accuse me? I couldn't have afforded the thirty-thousand-pound wedding if it wasn't for my parlour job. I've taken us on holiday to Australia, Hong Kong, the Maldives, Thailand, and paid for the lot. I pay all the bills and I bought him the fucking work van he drives around in."

Her fiancé won't let himself see how she truly earns the money because it helps them lead a comfortable lifestyle. She's debating quitting after she's married, but how will she ever survive if she leaves? She has to support two young children and her fiancé has a small DIY business that doesn't exactly bring home the bacon, so how can he keep their heads above water? Angel, unlike me, comes from an upper-middle-class family, so she hasn't been born into poverty, but she still has a craving for the money, living lavishly, buying her children designer school shoes. If she quits working, she'll also need to quit the spending sprees in designer stores.

*

Mark sits up, naked, on the divan. Gleaming white teeth. Grinning widely. "I think I love you." I don't understand this man. Is he deluded? Isn't he supposed to love his wife? Isn't that why he married her? Saying 'I love you' isn't a simple figure of speech. I've never serviced this man in my life before today and he thinks he loves me? Don't get me wrong, he's attractive—the type of guy anyone would fall for, any day of the week—if you disregard the fact he visits this sex house and has a wife. He dresses in a designer suit, matching cufflinks, tie and polished shoes. His hair is mousy blonde and immaculately groomed, he has vibrant, bright blue eyes, with the most tanned gorgeous skin and a cute posh accent. I can only describe him as candyfloss melting in my mouth. I want to indulge him, but Mark has one blinding weakness, and that's paying prostitutes, like many others, which can be a hard habit to break.

I don't want to destroy the heat of our moment by saying, "You think you love me, but you have a wedding ring on your finger." That would be a major passion killer. I'm not being paid to question his actions. I'm being paid to satisfy.

A lot of men talk openly about their wives. "I'll have to make an excuse to the wife, say I was stuck in traffic, or stuck in a meeting—or go in a bad mood with her and start an argument, so she stops asking questions as to why I'm late home," Mickey says. He's my four-thirty booking.

In my view, Mickey's bang out of order with his lame excuses. James, another regular, is the same. "I told my wife I went to the superstore, that's why I'm late home."

I've heard all sorts of crap excuses, like, 'I'm going to take a walk, for exercise. I'll be back in a couple of hours." Or, "I saw a friend I hadn't seen for ages, so we went for a few pints at the pub," or "I ended up driving to a drive-through to get some food. Fancied a change in food, even though I knew I'd be stuck in rush hour traffic. Oh well, you're not angry, are you? I'll still eat dinner with you."

And then there's the "I lost a hundred and twenty quid today, it must have fallen out of my pocket. I'm always dropping money. Daft, aren't I?"

I wonder how many women don't want to know the truth, and just prefer to go along with their excuses.

Many clients are lovely though, they really are—not all of them have complicated relationships—often they just genuinely don't have a girlfriend and they want company. It's not all about sex, too—that's just a small part of it. Maybe they feel I'm the nearest they can get to a girlfriend. I've got some lovely regulars who pay me to just have a cuddle.

CHAPTER NINE

What with work and feeding and caring for the feral colonies, trapping and neutering cats, vet appointments, carrying out home checks, finding foster parents and even fur-ever homes for cats I've got back on track, I just don't have the time for serious dating. I suppose without having a serious boyfriend, I find myself enjoying the time with clients. The orgasms are appreciated.

Pretty Ricky stands by the booking-in desk, waiting to be served. He has a light-brown skin tone and is clothed in a light-blue shirt, a part-suede jacket and smartly ironed skinny jeans with soft leather loafers. I notice he takes pride in his appearance: flawless.

"Alright, darlin'," Pretty Ricky overexaggerates a cockney accent, deliberately cavalier as he places his wallet on the reception desk.

I learn he works for an estate agent selling expensive properties. He has all the qualities of a buoyant salesman. He can talk the talk. As he undresses for me, he places an incredibly bling watch on the side.

We French kiss passionately up against the shower cubicle.

As I go to pass him a dry towel, he understands me. My heart begins to race.

"Do you work out?" I see he has an eight pack.

"Now and then, darlin'." He's drying down his naked body. "Come here." He draws my body towards his again and kisses me, more deeply this time. Shaking things up, he throws a pillow on the carpeted floor away from us. "I want to fuck you on the floor." His confidence is attractive, sending a ripple effect over me.

"I bet you do." I slide my panties down and off, kneel on the floor and begin to crawl towards the pillow.

"Fuck me, that arse." He puts on the rubber, gliding it down himself, watching my naked rear move away from him. He seats himself down on the corner chair for a few moments as I rest my head back on the pillow. He then lifts my backside upwards, so my sex is closer to him, with both my arms by my side for support. Getting me in the mood, he licks his fingers and teasingly flicks my sex, then slowly slides his hard-on inside me. He goes at it slow then begins to pound me fast and deep, pulling up my backside with each downward thrust so he can have me deeper. He's sexing me hard, and I'm moaning in ecstasy as he throbs inside me. An intense sensation of euphoria blasts over my body as I orgasm.

"Have you come?" he asks.

"Yes."

"I'm going to come too then." And he does. "Sorry if I was quick, I bust my nut, darlin'."

"It was fun." Blimey, he was quick, I wouldn't have minded a bit more of that.

"That's never happened to me before, darlin'." He sounds

pleased with himself. "Do you always come that quickly, Cat?"

"Not in here, no."

"I'm chuffed."

There's something magnetic between us. It makes me yearn for the connection I could have with a proper boyfriend, a little stab of regret in my heart that I'm preventing myself from meeting The One.

"Is it alright if I take another shower, darlin'? I'd love to take you out one night, babe, or even in the daytime for lunch. What do you say?" His proposal is attractive.

"Is that so? Where would you take me?" I'm intrigued, but I know I shouldn't be, as he's a client.

"I'd take you to the moon and back if I could. Lunch and a shop, or a lavish meal at night if you fancy? No sex. That's not what I'm about, darlin'. I want to get to know you. Look, I'll give you my number, alright? You don't have to call me. You can message me one time when you have a free afternoon."

Maybe his offer appeals to me because I'm beginning to crave someone who knows my secret, someone male, and someone who won't judge. Pretty Ricky doesn't seem to want to tie me down or sabotage me working in this place, and he doesn't seem as obsessed as some clients.

After he leaves, I ponder over his mobile phone number in the changing room. The following day, I message him:

Hi, it's Cat. x

I don't want to seem too keen by saying too much. Shit, I gave a client my real mobile number. Maybe Ricky won't reply. Best if he doesn't.

He does.

I'm chuffed you contacted me. You free tomorrow day? I know this nice Italian restaurant. You'd love it there. Let's make it a Leo Sayer. x

He wastes no time.

What's a Leo Sayer? And yes, I'm free at about 2 pm. x

Leo Sayer is an all-dayer. Whew, can't wait to see you, sexy lady. x

He's stood outside the Italian when I get there. Inside, while we eat, we talk about life, interests and future dreams. He leads the conversation and sees me as his conquest, making me laugh at every given opportunity. Possibly, he's able to meet up with me because he's on a weekly work-related trip up from London. Maybe I'm concealed from his London life, like a mistress would be, although he hasn't said he has a wife or kids in London.

After lunch we part ways. I now sense he was speaking honestly when he said he didn't want to use my body for a free sexing. I feel reassured and safe. Two days later we meet for an evening meal.

"I come into the parlour because I'm single, you know. I have such a busy work schedule, travelling up and down England. The parlour isn't really my scene. I only go there to get safe, no-strings sex, you know." He sips a glass of triple brandy and cola.

"Oh, right."

"I'm ready to settle down with the right lady, now. A decent girl." He peers deeply into my eyes. "I don't judge you, Cat."

"Thank you." I give him back the deep eye contact he needs, waiting for his next words.

"Look, this is how I see it. You work there, it's safe and it's clean. You get your money to live and go home. Simple."

For once, I feel I'm understood by someone of the opposite sex. He kisses me on my cheek, walks me to my car so he knows I'm safe, like a gentleman should, and I'm smitten.

But the next day, I get a shock when I browse through work's website, 'Mug Shot' list, which shows the faces of those men barred for being aggressive, abusive, dangerous, or causing criminal damage. . . Ricky's face appears.

'Goes by the name of Ricky, stole hundreds of pounds from a girl at another parlour. When the girl left the bedroom to get him a drink of water, which he had asked for, he stole all her earned wages from her purse, which she had left in the bedroom. He then informed the girl he couldn't have a service and rushed off, taking her money with him. He then phoned the parlour up later that day to inform the receptionist that he had mistakenly left his bank card in the room. He was testing the water to see if he had been detected for being a thief and to check if he had been barred.'

I should end our outside meetings at this point, but I'm confused because he doesn't seem like he could do something like that, being a gentleman and all. But if he did, then I want to confront him about his shifty, thieving ways. I never inform the boss that I've discovered one of my regulars is barred from another parlour. She would bar him from her premises too, and make sure everyone was aware never to let him book in with me or anyone else again. I kind of don't want him to be barred, not just yet anyway, as I do still like him.

Five nights later I let him take me out for a Chinese meal. After the meal (and a few drinks), we're kissing and holding hands as we walk, touching each other intimately at every opportunity. Onlookers would think we were in a serious relationship.

"Do you want to have one or two drinks back at my hotel apartment?"

"Yes, but then I'll have to go home. I've got to spend tomorrow morning doing a home check for a cat."

"Cool, babe. You'll love the hotel."

As he closes the hotel room door behind us, I say what's on my mind. "I heard you stole hundreds of pounds from a girl at another branch, and that you're barred. There's even a picture of you on the computer."

"What? Where's this picture of me? What does it say?"

"That you're barred for stealing from that girl."

"Well, I haven't stolen any money off anyone, darlin', so that's a lie. It must have been some other guy." His eyes appear angry.

"Oh, right then, if you say so. I wasn't going to say anything, but it's been on my mind."

"Bollocks. It's not true, babe." He storms out onto the hotel balcony, returning thirty seconds later. "Right, that's it. I've got a mate who's a solicitor. I'm going to phone him now and see what he says about getting them fuckers done for defamation of character."

"It's not a site that anyone else can see from outside of work. It's on an internal system, so I don't think you can get the owners in trouble for defamation. Defamation cases generally succeed if a person's name is tarnished within the public eye." I learnt this from my sister.

"But it wasn't me, babe. I'm not having my name being ruined."

"It's okay. You've seen me plenty of times and they've never mentioned to me that you're barred. Nobody recognises you from the picture."

"You don't believe I did it, do you? I don't look like a thief, do I? Do you think I look like a thief?"

"No, Ricky," I tell him. "I don't believe you could do something like that." I'm not sure what to believe. Perhaps he was mistaken for someone else.

"Good, babe, that's all that matters to me." He begins to trace kisses down my neck.

After sex, I smile at him. I like the feel of him inside me. He smiles back, kisses me on my chest then goes back into the bathroom to shower.

"Come join me, babe."

I follow him. We shower together. "You can sleep here tonight, Cat. I'll set my alarm for you if you want to wake up early."

Throughout the night, he caresses my body under the sheets. "I think I'm falling in love with you," he whispers.

Around midnight he asks, "Babe. Do you want a glass of water?"

I nod. He kisses my shoulder and walks out of the dark bedroom into the kitchen. I overhear him talking in a normal tone on his mobile phone.

"Yes, baby, I'm missing you too. Don't worry. I have to be here for work, you know that. Right. . . Yep. . . I'll phone you tomorrow then, baby. . . Love you too. Night."

So, he is a liar. He wanted to use me for sex even though he'd said he didn't, and it seems he doesn't want to pay. I'm no unpaid mistress. If I'm to date a man outside of work, it will have to be for love. I'm not playing second fiddle to any woman. At our first meal together, he showed me a picture of a little girl standing by the side of his mother. He told me she was his little sister. Now I wonder whether it was his daughter. Maybe he has a wife and child in London. On his return to the bedroom he passes me a cool glass of water.

"Love you, babe," he whispers. "Night."

I do not reply. His words no longer mean anything to me. I've learned a painful lesson. I will never allow myself to be used for free sex again, not with any client. I will never become a cheap man's mistress. I cannot demand an explanation from him. My occupation is to have sex with many different men, so why am I upset that he's sleeping with someone else? I have no right to be hurt or feel used. It's just the brazenness of him. He deserves a slap.

I pretend to fall asleep. I shouldn't kick off; it's pitch-black outside so I don't fancy walking alone in the city centre back to my car.

We don't have morning sex, despite his urging. I'll not permit my body to be used anymore by this sham of a man.

"Why don't you save your energy for the next time we meet?"

He walks me to my car like a true gentleman. He's acting genuine, but he's fake. Maybe he does have feelings for me and is genuinely attracted to me. Intimacy can create an unexplainable bond between two people; this is something I have come to learn.

Sexy lady, I loved every minute of our date. Again sometime, yeah? x

I ignore.

Hey, babe. I'm going to be in town. Are you free to see me outside of work tomorrow night? X

I fob him off.

You should visit me at work. I'm busy working overtime and have family commitments to tend to.

I think he gradually gets the hint because I don't see him at the parlour for at least three months, and then randomly, out of the blue, he walks in while I'm on a shift, having made no reservation.

I hear his distinctive London accent and my stomach tangles in loops. "Is Cat free?"

"No, love, she's not free for the next four hours."

I hide in the ladies' changing room, peering at his edgy movements through the gap between the saloon doors. One of my other clients is waiting for me in my boudoir, but I'll hang on till Ricky slings his hook before I go upstairs.

"Err, okay. . . Who else is free now?"

"Sunshine's free right now, also Jessie, Felisha and Laura."

"I'll see Sunshine." He's going with any random woman because I'm not free? He's a joke.

When Ricky walks upstairs to undress for Sunshine another girl informs me that she dated Ricky years ago outside of the workplace. I sit down and draw my knees up to my torso on the carpeted floor. This is another shock to my system. I take a breath and wait until he is well inside room number three, then I walk towards my boudoir.

Later, Ricky messages my mobile when I'm at home. He knows I've been at work up until nine, but he doesn't know I spotted him in the reception area.

Hi, babe. How are things? Are you working this weekend? I'm coming on business and would like to see you. Xx

I can feel rage travelling through me. He is totally unaware I saw him book in for sex with one of my co-workers. He's not having free sex from me at the weekend. I want to reply that I know he has a partner and that he should stop mithering me. Yet my stomach summersaults. I have no proper proof he has a wife or a daughter. He does wear a silver ring, but on his right hand. I suppose he could've moved it so I didn't notice he's married. I don't want to be pestered by this deceitful man any longer. What do I say to stop him?

Hi Ricky. I have a boyfriend now, so I won't be able to meet up with you anymore. Sorry.

I then change my mobile number.

CHAPTER TEN

"Kiss my feet now, or else." Alegra is dominant.

"Yes, mistress."

Her boudoir is a dungeon of domination and brisk pleasure. She entertains with handcuffs, butt plugs, dildos, strap-ons, whips, chains and a selection of lubricants. In the corner of her room is a selection of outfits ranging from PVC to the innocent schoolgirl. She's well prepared for most fantasies. She's a professional in this business—an attractive, middle-aged, auburn-haired lady, with a fantastic figure that she constantly hones, with FF breasts and the whitest veneers I've ever seen. She may not be as young as some of the others in here, but she never gets bad reports.

The Prince, as Alegra names him, is about five foot in height. We peer down at him because we're wearing heels.

"Humiliate me," he squeals, mouse-like and submissive, leaning back on Alegra's divan.

"If you wish, you dirty little boy." Alegra slaps him across his left cheek, yanking his beard towards her.

"Yes, mistress, yes, humiliate me. . . humiliate me," he begs.

"We're going to humiliate you alright, just wait." I prod him, kneeling on the bed next to him.

"Turn around. I'm going to smack your bot, you naughty. . . naughty. . . naughty. . . little. . . boy!' Alegra slaps him in time with the words. "Naughty." Slap. "Naughty." Slap. "Naughty." Slap.

He's Alegra's favourite big spender, her committed regular, and she's known him years.

Alegra gathers a mouthful of her saliva and spits onto his privates, slurping it back into her mouth before spitting it back onto his stomach. What on earth is she doing that for? She sucks it back off his body and aims it a little further up his stomach, towards his face. Eventually she takes in the spit, leans over him and puts it right into his mouth. He loves it.

"Lick my nipples. Now!" I order, undoing my leopard-print leotard, almost suffocating him with my breasts.

"Yes, mistress, anything you say, anything."

"Let's share him, Cat," Alegra says, as she gyrates on his leg.

I make my way down Alegra's bed. He's watching us from every angle, ceiling mirrors, wall mirrors, and face to face. She licks the right side of his dick and I mirror her movements on the left side. Our eyes engage as she rubs the side of my boob, and in that moment I know she wants girl-on-girl.

"Prince, wank off for me, while Cat and I play with each other. Do it, bastard. I want to see you wanking." Alegra bends me over in an awkward position, sideways, head down—I'm no gymnast.

I assume she's going to lick the side of my butt cheek, but she full-on licks my sex, then moves her tongue up to my arse. It tickles. It's divine. I rotate to face her, kissing her lips, and caressing her expensive fake breasts. It's not often I get the chance to play with another female. Keeping powerful eye contact with him, I keep kissing her, putting my tongue in her mouth. It tastes minty. She rubs my sex softly in a clockwise motion, making me moist, then she places her hand at the back of my neck, pushing her tongue deeper into my mouth.

I slap her bottom. "Let's get Prince involved." Making my way back over to him, I sit my sex on his admiring face. He's not instinctively skilled at oral. Maybe he hasn't had much practice. I probably would've been better off sitting on her face.

"Go on. Lick her cunt. You dirty bastard," Alegra yells angrily at Prince.

This service is three hours long. For heaven's sake, he'd better pay me well.

With Prince on his back, Alegra begins her spitting again, then licks his arse without even asking if he'll pay the extra. Rimming is a costly speciality. Oh well, she knows him better than I do. He's a 'wadded Prince from a foreign land', or so she told me. I lift off his face, sliding two fingers inside Alegra, giving him his money's worth.

"Prince, Cat is fingering me. Watch."

"Yes, mistress Alegra." He lifts his head, doing as he's told.

What the heck is she doing to me now? She's tying my hair up in a lopsided messy ponytail whilst I'm playing with her. Maybe she wants to be domineering over both of us, but no, I am my own boss. I smile politely but untangle my hair. He's transfixed, watching our girl-on-girl playtime, so he doesn't notice any awkwardness. How would she like it if I took a handful of her hair and shoved it up? Alegra begins to wrap her own bobble around his ballsack and he smiles, watching her do it. So, the bobble she just put in my hair could've gone up someone's backside for all I know—fucking great.

"You're being a good boy, aren't you? It's time to get really naughty." Slap. Slap. She assertively slaps his balls.

"Yes. Yes. Yes. Please. Please. Humiliate me."

Alegra and I devour his hard-on. She sucks him first, then pulls off, and I suck him, then pull off. Her again, and then me again, Her. Me. Her. Me. Her. Me. Her.

"Girls, oh, yes, girls."

"Shut up, you son of a bitch." She picks up a large rubber strap-on and pulls the straps over her waist-length auburn hair and positions it on her crotch. She grabs a tub of lube and a condom, places it over the dildo, douses it in lube and then immerses it in his arse. He doesn't show any signs of discomfort. How can this be? Has he had anal from Alegra before? Most probably, by the look of it.

"Take it. Take it. Take. It." She's getting rough with him. She hasn't even asked him for permission, no approval to intrude in his arsehole.

"Yes, boss. Yes. Yes. I will," he groans, worshipping Alegra.

"You will what?"

"I will take it, mistress. Anything you say."

"Yes, you fucking will. You'll take it. You'll take it." She's slamming her strap-on into him over and over again. I can literally hear the banging noise of her torso knocking against his body. Knock. Knock. Thwack. This isn't just any threesome.

I lick my lips, suck his nipples hard, and then clamp down on them with my teeth. He's still on his back and she's still going at it.

"Oh, yes, I like that," she whispers into my ear. She likes it when I hurt him.

I twist his nipples and he yells in full pleasure.

"Thank you. Give me pain. Nipple-twist me more."

"I'm the boss, not you. You will obey me. You will do what I say."

"Anything you say, Cat. I will obey you."

"Yes. You. Will. You'll listen to me. I'm going to punish you because you're a bastard."

"Please. I want punishment."

"I'll give you punishment when I want to, not when you want it." Alegra takes the strap-on out. She might start to beat him with it—fuck knows, she's a madwoman.

"Bend over, you fucker." She moves over to me on the divan, placing the strap-on over my head. Shit, I've never used one of these before.

"Go on, Cat, fuck him, fuck him hard," she dictates, "make him take it."

Reaching out for a fresh condom I roll it down the strap-on. Really, I want to ask him if he's okay with this, but if I do it'll portray me as submissive, and I must carry on humiliating him. It's what he wants—his words, not mine. So, I cover the condom with lube. Here goes. I push it deep inside him.

"Do you like that? You're so fucking dirty. Take it, take this big gun." I step up my game. 'You're our fucking cunt."

"Yes, he is, he's our fucking cunt. Fucking bastard cunt."

Alegra forces my body into him, which pushes the strap-on deeper. 'Harder. Harder. Give it to him. Harder, she screams out, tossing back her hair.

"Yes, fuck me harder."

Give it him harder? Hasn't he had enough of this butt fucking? Clearly not. Surely time's nearly up? Turning my body around I check the clock.

"We have one hour left," I let them know.

I thrust him twenty or so more times, then he says, "I need to have a rest."

"Of course." I pull out the strap-on, giving him a rest.

"Would you girls mind if I get dressed?" he asks us.

"If you must, Prince," she allows.

He begins to dress. "I'm going to pop outside for a moment. I want a cigarette and refreshment." He wipes the sweat from his brow.

"We'll wait here for you." I smile.

He moseys out of the dungeon, and I turn to Alegra. "Is he okay?" I ask.

"Yes, he's fine. He always has a break in the middle of a service."

"Oh, right. I wonder how much he'll give us?"

"You'll be surprised, gorgeous."

We glance at each other and stroke each other's legs, then giggle. We're both flirty. All we want is our due money—pay up sucker.

I shower, and then wait for his so-called highness to reappear. Alegra clears the empty condom wrappers and takes pride in the layout of her room, laying clean towels down neatly over the satin sheets, ready for his return.

"Alegra, I'll be back in a minute; I need to check my phone. I had a missed call before I came upstairs."

"Sure, honey."

I ring the cat rescue back.

"I have a favour to ask of you," the branch coordinator says.

"Okay."

"Can you take a cat and release her with the rest of the colony?"

"Why? Is she feral?" I can't just release any cat out in the wild.

"Yes, she is. She attacked the vet, and they think she should either be put to sleep or released, and if she can't go with the feral cats you feed, I'm going to have to put her to sleep." She starts to cry.

I can't let this happen. "I will take her, but she'll need to be familiarised with the area. What if she runs away and ends up lost? The colony need to be given a chance to accept her, too."

I need to think about what to do.

Ten minutes later, the Prince returns and he is clearly ready for round two. He hasn't finished off yet, so it's our duty to get the job done. He strips his clothes off and takes a quick shower before parking his body back beside us on the divan. Alegra takes her frilly leather knickers off and puts them on him—she's insane. She yanks her knickers right up so that the G-string presses up against his crack and balls. Oh my! You wouldn't catch me doing that with my knickers.

"Humiliate me," he cries, "humiliate me."

"Everyone can see you're wearing my thong. You naughty, naughty, naughty boy. Touch yourself!" Everyone? Alegra must be insinuating there's a make-believe crowd in the room when there's clearly not. I suppose it adds to his mounting tension.

"Yes, you, naughty, naughty boy!" I shout, slapping his backside. "Do as you're told. Naughty." Slap. "Naughty." Slap. "Naughty." Slap. "Naughty." I continue slapping him. Slap. Slap. Slap.

"Yes, tell me what to do?" He yelps.

"Lick Alegra's arse, you dirty boy."

He licks, as he's ordered.

Time's almost up. I best act quick, do something to make him finish. I toss him off alarmingly quickly, and he cannot help but squirt out of the side of her thong—hooray.

"Time's up, Alegra." I make it clear, so she knows I need my payment.

"Thank you, ladies. I'll have another shower." He stands.

Alegra and I shower after him. We all begin to re-dress.

It's been an incentive to work harder—I need the money to go towards my business plan. Not to mention my younger brother, Adonis, who's now studying at college and needs his driving lessons paying for. Then, when he passes, he'll need a car, not forgetting his insurance, MOT and road tax. My family needs my help. I hope Prince tips as well as Alegra has promised.

Adonis is ten years younger than Kitty and has a different father to us. Adonis is brilliant—he's studying to be a physicist and I will do anything I can to help him make it.

Alegra puts her knickers back on after he had them up between his buttocks and had his dick and balls all over them. I'm slightly surprised. She doesn't mention payment to him.

I normally mention cost to clients but this time I'll stay quiet because she obviously knows him well.

He pulls out a large wodge of money and counts what looks like half out for Alegra and half for me. I don't need to count it right now; it's obviously a significant amount.

"Here's my number, Cat. Alegra has it already. I tell her if she ever leaves here then she can still contact me for business and I'll meet her."

"Fab idea, Prince, I'll save it in my phone. Goodbye, lovely to meet you. Hope to meet you again."

Then it hits me—he's right. I need to start taking clients' numbers for when I leave here to set up alone. They'll all need to know the location of my new parlour once I've found one.

"Mwah. See you soon, naughty boy," Alegra says, lightly slapping his face. She puts on a spectacular show. I might take a leaf out of her book and buy a strap-on to fuck clients with. I draw the line at putting my underwear on them, though.

Prince leaves, and we dash back to the lobby. I don't want to be another minute over for Denny, my next booking. In the ladies' changing room I pull my locker key out of my bag and start to count the payment. Flicking through the notes, I know I can now pay for Adonis's driving lessons.

"He gave us both a big tip," I tell Fran, one of the other workers. 'That's bumped my earnings up. How much have you done so far, Fran?"

"Not as much as you."

"Oh, no. Well, I hope your day gets better."

"Another parlour has just opened a few streets away, you know. I think that's going to affect business here."

"That's fast, only the other week Wonderful House closed down and now another has replaced it?"

"Yes, it is fast."

"I'm fully booked all day."

"You best make the most of it then, while you can."

She's right. Today's been a walk in the park so far. The others must be jealous of Alegra and me, but it's not our fault they haven't had an influx of clients or received a large tip off a prince. If another parlour has just opened, my next shift could be dire. This job has a shelf life, so getting telephone numbers is a positive step towards keeping my clients once I've left here—you've got to stay business minded.

*

I collect the cat that the charity has asked me to take from the vet. I name her Scarlett. I don't think she's ever had a name in her life so now she is even more precious. I don't know much about her background, just that she'd previously been caged up for years, apparently in a hoarding situation, although I'm not sure how true that is. I release her at the derelict barn cats colony after allowing her five days of getting her familiarised with the area, carrying her round in a cat carry case, showing her where the other cats outdoor feeding stations are, letting her watch them eat. Usually, cats are supposed to be conditioned for about four weeks to the area before they're released in a crate with food, water and litter; a week often suffices but because of Scarlett's past it needs to be a quick transition.

I don't see Scarlett coming for food every day so when she begins to appear daily, it's lovely to see her sitting alongside her lookalike, Beauty, who we'd often get her mixed up with. I notice Scarlett is poorly, with what looks like an exploded eye; blood and green, infected pus is leaking out of her eye and nose. Two veterinary nurses come to the colony to look at her eye as we've struggled to catch her, which is lovely of them, but no luck, they couldn't get close enough to see if her eye needs removing. It takes weeks, but we finally manage to catch her in a drop trap and have her looked over and tested at the vets. She comes back FeLV-positive, which is feline leukaemia, and I am asked if I want her to be put to sleep. I decline. She has to have her teeth removed and is put on antibiotics and Bisolvon to help clear her airways. In cats, leukaemia is contagious unless they are vaccinated against it.

Indoors, every day for months, even after work shifts, I sit with Scarlett and try to build a bond with her. I grow to love her dearly. She won't allow a single stroke, but blinks slowly in my presence. In cat language that's a good sign. She isn't getting any better, though, and can't fight the flu, much as I try to help her. Her breathing becomes laboured, and she coughs and sneezes out bloody gunk. I am devastated I can't do any more to help her.

In the end, Scarlett grows her angel wings, and now rests in peace without pain.

At the vets, the nurse says, "Would you like to hold her?"

I burst into tears. "Please."

The vet nurse kisses the slightly sedated Scarlett before she hands her to me, which is lovely. She doesn't know Scarlett, and she knows she's FeLV-positive and has cat flu. I kiss and cuddle Scarlett too, and say, "Goodbye, Scarlett. I love you so much. I'm so sorry." Tears flood from my eyes and my sister,

Kitty, asks if I want her to take pictures of me holding Scarlett, as a reminder. Kitty cries. Everyone in the room, including the vet, has tears in their eyes.

I have Scarlett's paw prints, whiskers, fur and ashes at home, and I will always love and think of her. She may not have had much human interaction in her lifetime, but at least she left this world knowing she was loved.

CHAPTER ELEVEN

"Cat, the guy who's booking in with you at the desk is a client I know. He's called Gerald on your booking sheet. He likes role play." One of the girls on shift giggles. "He'll treat you as if you're in his director's office for a porn interview and he'll pretend he's filming the whole conversation behind an imaginary rolling camera. He'll ask you what fantasies you want to fulfil as an up-and-coming porn star. He probably wishes he was a porn director."

Just as she predicted, he's pretending to hold a camera in my face when I enter the Egyptian Room, and he's naked.

"Do you like foreplay? Do you let others watch?" he asks.

"Yes. I love it all," I answer in a high-pitched voice, acting like I'm a playboy bunny, posing for his fake camera. I name him Camera Roll Guy.

"Can you tell me why you want to be a porn star so much?"

"Because I love sex and pleasing men, and I think it's amazing if any sexy girl can make a career out of it."

"Do you take it up the arse?"

"Oh, yes. The naughtier, the better." I giggle and flick my hair.

"Would you perform any girl-on-girl action?" His fake camera is right in my face now.

"I would love to." I wink at the fake camera.

"You've passed the interview with flying colours, Cat. Can you begin straight away?" He walks over to his briefcase and takes out two sets of brand-new underwear.

"I can begin straight away, yes."

"Here, try these on for size."

They are exquisite pieces of lingerie. I like what I see. The first set I try on still has a price tag on it. It's a two-piece, full bra and silky crotchless thong, which feels unbelievably luxurious against my skin. The second is a one-piece black lace bodysuit. Again, the price tag is still attached. I'll be extra nice to him, hoping he'll allow me to keep this stuff.

"I've purchased your specific bra size, just for you. I looked at your online profile to see your measurements before I bought them."

"Thank you, darling, I love them. Shall I remove the tags?"

"No, no. They aren't for you to keep."

He will probably return them to the store to get a refund. The cheek of him!

"Bend over, Cat."

"Yes, sir."

"Call me sergeant."

"Yes, sergeant."

"Touch yourself for the camera."

"Sergeant, you're making me nervous holding that camera. I've never done a porn movie before."

"I'll get you in hundreds of my porn movies."

"Oh, will you now? As long as you're involved too, sergeant."

"I'll be right inside you, filming it all."

"You're the boss. Whatever floats your boat, sarge."

"Turn back around, Cat."

"No problem."

"Now, open your legs and sit on the edge of the bed. Look at the camera."

"Okay."

"Talk for the camera, Cat."

"What do you want me to say?"

"Tell them your age. Introduce yourself. Where you come from."

"Right. My name's Cat, everyone. I'm in my mid-twenties. This is my first porn movie, guys, so I'm new to this."

"Brilliant. Where are you from, Cat?"

"I'm from heaven."

"You certainly are angel. Now suck on me, dirty angel." He tilts his imaginary camera down towards his hard-on, rolling the imaginary handle forwards, round and round. It must be a make-believe Victorian cine camera.

"Let me see your tongue sliding down my shaft," he instructs, still peering down his make-believe camera lens.

I extend my tongue towards him, fluttering my lashes whilst wanking him on my tongue. My knees are feeling the pressure of the hard tiles.

"Why don't we get on the bed? Rest the camera on the side to film us."

"Hmm, yes."

"Take me doggy." Not many men I know can refuse that offer.

"That peachy arse, boy oh boy. I'm hard as fuck, girl."

On all fours, I turn back to check what he's up to. He rests his make-believe camera down on the bedside cabinet, looking back to see if it definitely is aiming our way for the porno scene.

"Slide yourself inside me. This'll be the first porn movie I've fucked in."

"Show the camera you're enjoying it."

I smile for the camera. Some may think this is ludicrous, but I find it fun. I push back on him, then forward, and then slam my bottom back on him.

Easy. Done. All over.

"Oh. Oh. Err. . . I wanted to last longer than that." He's upset.

"Longer? Well, this porn movie has been fun for me. I've had the best time with you."

"Have you? Great. I'm happy then. No doubt I'll be seeing you again, Cat."

"That's fine. You can check when I'm next here on the work website."

"My wife and I hardly have sex anymore, but we still live together. Would you be interested in dating an older man?"

Does he not understand the concept of marital commitment? It seems not. When does commitment come into play? I've been giving this subject some thought.

Here are my definitions of different types of relationships:

1. Fucking: no say. No time spent together. Purely straight sex.
2. Seeing Each Other: again, no say, but instead of straight sex, two people may spend time together, for example going to the movies; going out for dinner.

3. Relationship: this is a commitment to be together and to get to know each other on a deeper level. No cheating.
4. Engagement: the same level of commitment as the fifth and final stage, marriage. Please note: some individuals regard this as the last time they can have sexual relations with someone else other than their partner.
5. Marriage: self-explanatory.

Parlour girls are at stage number one with clients—purely straight sex—but some women in here date their clients outside of work, having no free time to lead a normal life and be in a normal relationship. But, being used for free isn't for me.

*

I'd thought that Leo-Nigel and Cassandra-Dior were the last kittens to appear at the barn cats colony, but one day as I am passing, I spot a small, black cat dart under an abandoned truck. It's about the same age as Tiger Lily's kittens would have been if they'd lived. It looks nothing like Tiger Lily—she was calico, and her kittens were ginger and calico—but it's possible this cat is hers. I can't tell whether it's a boy or a girl, but we decide to call he or she Blackberry.

At this point, I had named and counted fifty-three cats, which included the other colony I had started to feed, on an industrial estate. Paying for it all—food, vet bills, equipment—was still hard, but I knew the cats relied on me. I couldn't stop working, even if I wanted to, because I needed the funds. I do worry this job has a shelf life. How will I pay for the cats to eat if I'm out of work? So, I keep raising awareness for them on social media, and running a wish list for food and supplies. I don't work every day so income isn't steady, or guaranteed, so I set up a donation account, in case anyone felt they'd like to send a donation, they could do so. Having an online presence also brings me closer to like-minded people. I receive a lovely message from a kind supporter:

Hi, hope you don't mind me messaging you. Would you mind if I gave you a donation to help you care for all the cats you're looking after? You're truly a very special person that gives all you can to help these precious animals. God bless you—you are an angel.

And another kind message, from another cat friend:

I hope I chose the right food on online—do they send it to you? I am going to write a card about you in the book section of our shop unit and will continue to support with sales. By all means mention that we sent you cat food. I will share pictures at our book unit when we get it set up, so you get more publicity.

Sometimes a kind word at the end of a long day can mean just as much as a donation. Any help is some help, and the cats and I are always grateful.

CHAPTER TWELVE

Leading up to the winter, the unkind weather starts to set in, and with it comes unbearable thoughts about how many of the homeless colony cats will die. This is the time of year when I lose much-needed sleep as my worries about the colonies increase.

"Should I rent a house for them? I mean, I've not been working that much lately, but I can't bear to see them shivering in the snow again. It's just too cold for them," I say to my mum.

"No, you can't afford that."

"Well, I'll have to, because I can't cope with them being cold. I'll just have to do a few more shifts. They'll freeze to death, like Tiger Lily's kittens did last year. I've seen some places to rent in the area."

"Are they allowing pets, though?"

"I don't know. I'll keep it clean. Cats are clean generally. I'll train them to use litter trays, and if they're messy, I'll get new carpets and redecorate."

"I've got a spare room. Why don't you bring them here?"

"No, mum, it's too noisy at yours with the boys, and these feral cats aren't used to it."

"Just do it. You can't afford to rent somewhere else. I'll help feed them every day and keep the place clean."

She is right, really. I can't afford it. I'd thought I could just work a bit more, you know, sell my body. But renting a property for the cats would really dip into the food fund.

As I trap them and bring them in for the winter, I'm able to get them back to optimum health. I even decide not to put the vulnerable ones back out when it comes to re-releasing them. But mum doesn't find it as easy to be around the cats as I do.

"Can't you just clean the trays, mum? Just till I come over."

"They want to kill me," she laughs.

"Mum, don't be so silly. They don't want to kill you."

"As soon as I open that door, they start to hiss and growl. Arch their backs. They want to jump on my head."

"Mum, stop it." I giggle. "They'd never do that. They're more scared of you than you are of them. They're just trying to protect themselves, and most of them will just hide from you."

"Look, when I go over to the dining-room window to open it, Petal looks at me with those eyes."

Mum has only ever had socialised cats. The feral, wild-born cats are a bit different to house cats; well, at least at first. But there's no need to be put off. They just need a little TLC to gain their trust. And when it's time for the vets, you can't just pick them up—you need to really know what you're doing. Most vets wear gauntlets when handling feral cats. I have some of those gloves, and not just for handling feral cats—I need them for handling some of my clients!

Emanuel is a feral I take to the vets after I trap him to bring him in for winter. It's protocol with all the cats I trap. I also have him tested for FIV and FeLV. The result wasn't good.

"I'm sorry, but he's tested positive for both FIV and FeLV. You have the option to put him to sleep." The vet waits for my response.

My head sinks into my hands. Not this again, after Scarlett having had FeLV.

"No. He's always looked healthy." I wipe away my tears. I'd never even heard of half of the issues cats can have until I decided to trap and neuter the feral cats. Some say cats are free souls, but they shouldn't have to struggle through the winter months; this is why I do what I do. And thanks to some of my lovely social media friends with their advice and previous experience, I have hope in things like false positives, so I ask about having Emanuel retested. But my only option is a lab test, which has a high price tag attached.

"Two hundred and fifty pounds?" Damn it.

"Or, like I said, you have the option to put him to sleep."

"No, I'm not even considering that." I guess I'll just have to put in some more hours at work to fund this. Even if his lab test still says he's positive there's no way that should be a death sentence for him in my eyes.

Do you think it's costly trying to feed one or two cats? Or ten? Twenty? Thirty? You're really pushing the boat out now. Try *sixty*, and you'll get a sense of how I feel. How on earth would anyone afford this on a minimum-wage job? Most would be into their overdraft, spent up on their credit cards, getting into debt, selling sentimental items. What about all the cat litter? Jeez. And the vet's bills. Sore subject. To me, paying for pet insurance just isn't doable for each of them. But no one else has the cats' backs the way I do. I try my hardest to make ends meet, and they're as well looked after as they can be, food-wise—better than most. If they're in need of veterinary care, which they often are, we have to sort it somehow, even if that means tossing off a few gents.

Thankfully, Emanuel's laboratory test comes back negative, so, like I knew, there is no need to put him to sleep. He can go back to his feline family.

*

"I've just done an out-call with the agency," my friend Cynthia says over the phone. She works as a call-girl for an agency.

"And? Spill."

"He was a lovely guy."

"That's good."

"Clean, easy to get along with."

"Go on."

"Well, he told me that his wife is always doing cat stuff."

Obviously, my friend knows I am too.

"Really! Gosh."

"He's from our area. Apparently, his wife is notorious in the cat world. He says they have tons of cats and she's hardly got any time for him, which is why he booked me."

"Oh, no. Well, he should raise that with her, but she must really be neglecting him. Still though, fucking hell. That's bad."

I wonder if his wife is someone I know, someone I've crossed paths with. Little did he know when he told my friend about his wife, he could be unwittingly revealing himself because I am also in the cat world.

I think I know who it is, but I'm not sure. And anyhow, I

can hardly go to her and say, "Is it your husband who's been having it off behind your back with escorts?"

I have to text Cynthia to get it off my chest, so I send her two pictures of my cat friend's husband that I retrieve off Facebook.

Is this the client you saw that day? I was thinking about his wife and whether or not I knew her? You said she's in the cat world. Don't worry, I won't say anything. x

She replied:

No, baby, he was older. x

The next day:

I've just realised it is the same guy on those pics! x

For fuck's sake.

Really? Oh no. x

He's lovely. x

Can't be that lovely if he's going behind his wife's back though. x

I reply.

Well, hun, when two people have been together for many years and the woman goes off sex and doesn't give her husband enough attention, the man still has testosterone that affects him. It's better to sort it quickly with a no-strings-attached deal to keep the relationship at home healthy. . . better to do that than have an affair. Sex is important. It keeps the mind sane. x

I can't stop thinking about it. I have to ring Cynthia. "Are you sure it's him?" I say quietly down the phone, as I walk down the aisle in the pet shop.

"Yes. I didn't realise the other day until I looked at the other pic you sent me, the one without the hat? I forgot he looks quite young for his age. He said he works in Manchester."

"Anything else you know about him?"

"What do you want to know?"

"How long did he book you for? An hour?"

"Yes. We didn't have sex, though. I just give him a hand job and he was very excited."

"You're crazy, Cynthia. Will call you later, I'm just at the till."

For some reason I'm disappointed at the sheer betrayal of this guy. I'm always busy with cats, too, and sometimes I don't get to bed till late, so maybe the guy's wife finds upkeep hard. This woman doesn't really know how much attention she should be giving her husband—I can clue her up in that department. Or perhaps it's an excuse on his behalf and he's always been the type to book call-girls? Maybe it's a fantasy of his. Maybe I'd see it differently if he was an escort himself, trying to make ends meet like I do, but the fact he's trying to make himself feel better by putting the blame on his wife and sharing her personal details with a girl he's paying to please him is worrying. Or maybe he just wants someone to talk to about his circumstances.

"Here." I'm handed a voucher by the lady at the till. "I'm not supposed to do this, but. . ."

I think I know what she means by 'but'. 'But' comes under a few meanings, to me.

But, I feel sorry for you buying all of this cat food for homeless cats.

But, it's the least I can do.

But, the cats need this twenty-five percent off. You'll be able to buy more cat food for your money.

But, something tells me I should give the voucher to you because I'm the girl who always serves you when you come into the store, and I know the cats cost you over a thousand a month, and the receipt I give you at the end of your bill is the longest I ever give anyone.

I often tell the pet shop staff how much of a struggle it is, but that I won't give up on the cats.

"How do you afford to buy all of this food for the feral cats?" The checkout girl says to me one day, waiting for a believable answer.

Sometimes, I wish I could tell the truth, but that would look bad, wouldn't it? I mean, it's a big thing for me, coming clean. Would they respect me if they knew? Look down on me? Would they help me as much? I don't see myself as any less of a person. I'm still me. The girl who helps feed hungry mouths.

"Oh, I just rent myself out for money." Would I say it like that?

"Well, I have this main client who pays me for my services." That doesn't sound too bad.

"What services would that be?" Their riposte, no doubt.

"Do you really want to know?"

I'm sure they'd get the drift then.

"Men pay me to look after them, you know." How does that sound?

See, it's a difficult one to explain. I'd be digging an even deeper hole.

"I mean, not everyone wants sex. I don't have to go down on every man or have *ménage à trois* in each booking. I'm paid for my time. There's lots of kissing involved, most of the time. Massages for me, and oral for me as well. I get a good time. Orgasms, that kind of thing."

Seriously—how, just how, do I come clean? For now, I just do what I've become used to doing for some time and keep my secret to myself.

CHAPTER THIRTEEN

I haven't seen Ocean—a silver tabby tom cat—for months. He hasn't appeared for food at any of the barn cats' feeding stations. I even phone the local recycling centre to check if he's hopped in a bin and been taken to the recycling plant. But I have a feeling—I know in my heart—that he's passed.

"That cat you've been looking for?" the farmer says as I'm dishing out food for the homeless barn cats. "I found it under a scrap car, dead."

"Whereabouts?" I ask.

"Over here, I'll show you."

The farmer is kind enough to allow me and my sister access to this part of his land. He probably thinks I'm a crazy cat lady.

"I saw it underneath the car when I was mowing the nettles down. So, I pulled it out and saw it was a dead cat. I'd usually just bin it but remember you saying you've been looking for a missing cat so thought I'd show you."

"Thank you."

The farmer walks off.

"Do you think it's Ocean?" I ask my sister.

"I can't tell for sure, but it looks like it could be him. I mean, look at the teeth. They're white, they look new—it's definitely a young cat."

"Oh, yes, and look at the ears. Not all the cats have long ears like that."

"Ocean had white whiskers too." I point at them.

"It must be him. How did he get to look like this? He looks mummified."

I bury Ocean in the area where the barn cats live.

I can't get over how Ocean's body looked stiff, and he had a black coating all over his body like he wasn't fully decomposed. It was so strange to see him preserved that way. I'm curious. How did Ocean end up this way? His body seems to have been left in the mud for months. With other corpses left out in the open, like Cassandra-Dior and Leo-Nigel, nature leaves nothing but bones and fur. But the shape of Ocean's body—even his tail and his ears—had been preserved. I hope that nothing untoward has happened to Ocean. I wish I knew. I guess I never will.

These cats suffer. Many of them have had cut paws from smashed glass because of all the abandoned trucks and cars dotted on the farmer's land. Many have parasites, and I have to deflea and deworm them regularly which, as you can imagine, costs a small fortune. And let's not forget the ticks.

"Is that a tick on Cinderella's head?"

"What the heck?"

"How do we get that off her?"

"Trap her first, and that's never a quick task."

We try to trap her for three days straight, hoping to get her to a vet, but by the fourth day, the tick had dropped off.

When four cats die in the space of only a few months, it becomes clear that no matter what we do, cats are going to die. We realise that we can't just leave them outdoors like this, especially in freezing temperatures. They need a safe haven on a long-term basis.

Each winter, I sob at their deaths, their cat flu, their breathing difficulties and their struggles. Already, I've lost Cassandra-Dior, Leo-Nigel, Lilly, Scarlett and Ocean, as well as a whole host of others: Blue Girl, Billy, Harry, Big Lad, Snowy, Edward, Priscilla and Dita. Each death hits us hard. All pass away for different reasons, but each reason is linked to—or as a direct consequence of—their outdoor living conditions.

Dita was mauled by a dog. I found her not far from the garage cats colony where she would lay her head down to rest at nights. I managed to put a tracker collar on Dita with her phone number on, because she had lived at the garage for so long, being fed by me, that she let me stroke her. This was a breakthrough—she'd learnt to trust human contact. But when the dog mauled her, the owner didn't even contact us. Heartless. She was full of dog bites, with the tracker collar slung about ten yards from her lifeless body. I buried her in my garden.

Billy was buried near his home in the barn cats colony. I think he was a victim of a road traffic accident. All year round, people race down the lane like rally drivers on bikes and in cars near the barn cats, knocking them down.

Or was Billy poisoned? Possibly, like Cassandra-Dior and Leo-Nigel might have been. Not everyone likes cats. But post-mortems are really expensive, and I can't afford that, and I know the cats that have passed would rather I spend money on food for their colony family. Even if a post-mortem discovered poison, who would I blame? Cats can even die from licking anti-freeze that's dripped out of a car.

I don't get a chance to bury ginger Harry because he was found near the barn cats colony by a passer-by, who told me they'd put him in a bin a couple of weeks after the accident.

Big Lad, a stray I left food out for at the garage cats colony, passed away because of anaemia and failing organs. He was finding it difficult to breathe so he had to be put to sleep. I needed to do the right thing to stop his suffering. I have his paw prints, and some of his fur and whiskers from before he was cremated.

*

One day, I get another kind message from one of my cat friends.

My mum lives in England and she's making all your cats some winter beds and blankets, and when they are all done, she will post them to you or she will get someone to drive her. I'll let you know when she's finished making them.

I reply:

That's absolutely lovely of your mum. Are you originally from the UK? And I can probably drive to your mum if she has made a lot of them. Is she knitting them? And how lovely of her to think of the homeless cats here. She's an absolute cat angel.

I hear back:

Yes, I lived in Warrington for 18 years before I came to the US 10 years ago. Mum still lives there; she wanted to make beds for cats where I live but postage is ridiculous and not worth it, so I said I know a lady in Manchester who rescues cats. I was sure you could use some, so she said she'd like to make them for you. She makes little quilted padded cotton beds and blankets, all are washable. Once she's got a stack made, I'll let you know.

I got another lovely message, in a condolence card.

Sorry for your recent losses. My heart goes out to you at this sad time. It's wonderful the lengths you go to to help unwanted strays and feral cats when most other people wouldn't care. There's surely a place in the afterlife for you magnificent girl for all you've done and continue to do for the forgotten ones. All my love.

All I want to do is give these innocent cats a better chance at life. I could offer them a safe haven to go to rather than being put to sleep, which is what a lot of vets advise and resort to when they come into contact with injured, stray or feral cats. And it's not just the feral cats that I feed—I hear of many homeless feral cat colonies. The scrapyard cats that are at risk of being crushed as they search for food amongst heavy machinery. The churchyard cats that live off rubbish, scrummaging through rubbish bags for mouldy leftovers. But for now, there's no safe place for larger colonies to go. Just like the barn cats and garage cats.

*

"Are there any ladies free for an hour now?"

"What? Now? You want to see someone for an hour right

now?" The receptionist checks through the girls' booking sheets for the day.

"Which girls execute domination?" he asks, looking at the pictures on the wall.

"All of the girls on today carry out domination, sir, it just depends what specialities you like?"

"Reverse anal and being tied up. I am very particular about my services. The lady must be willing to use some of my playthings. Is this feasible?" He pushes out his chest, alongside his bulging belly, lifting up his white carrier bag.

Watching him from above the changing room saloon doors, he looks like a farmer, wearing a caramel-coloured tweed jacket with matching brown pants and a white-buttoned shirt. He's well-built and aged around sixty, the sides of his hair a dusty brown with a balding patch on top. He has red, rosy cheeks.

He lifts his carrier bag above the desk so the receptionist can see what's inside.

"Plaited ropes?" She is shocked.

Ropes? I'll fucking tie the gentleman up.

"Hi, I'm Cat. I'm free to see you now, if you would like?" I saunter towards him confidently, placing my palms down on the desk, pushing out my breasts and arse.

"Glorious. She will do perfectly fine."

Tough luck to the other girls who have missed out on a one-hour booking by being unwilling to approach customers.

"What's your name?" the receptionist asks him.

"Harold." She passes Harold two rolled up peach-coloured towels. "Go to room number four and shower, and she'll join you shortly."

"I wouldn't want to spend an hour with him anyway, he looks tight with his money," one girl sneers as I walk back inside the changing room.

"He probably smells." A second girl smirks.

The truth is that in this game you never know which clients have money and which don't, which ones are big spenders and which are tight. I need this booking because I've just had to pay for Tiger Lily's emergency vet visit for jaundice, her liver markers were high due to an underlying viral infection, she had the runs and was dehydrated so needed fluids. Plus, Kitty's Land Law teacher told her she needs another two updated law books, amounting to £130. Plus, she tells me she needs to apply for the Bar Professional Training Course (BPTC) as this is what she needs to join, once she has completed the law degree, to become a barrister, but it's not cheap, it'll cost thousands. What average student can afford to splash over a hundred pounds on two books and thousands on a one-year course? I don't know of anyone other than my sister. But most prostitutes could afford to. Harold is wearing an expensive watch, so the chances are he has a bob or two.

I apply my shimmery lip gloss in the mirror, allowing him a few minutes to shower, before I head to my boudoir.

"Hello, Harold." I pass him a clean towel.

"Wonderful." He takes the towel. "I've not seen you here before. I guess today is my lucky day. I'll just set up my belongings."

I watch him curiously, standing near the closed boudoir door.

"Do you need my help, Harold?"

He ignores my question, mumbling to himself. "Now then.

If I put this here, then maybe it will hold." He is attaching his thick ropes to each corner of the bed.

"Let's get started then, Cat. Can you tie up my hands and feet with the other ends of my ropes?"

"Yes, of course, sweetheart." I do as he asks.

"Tie me down so I can't get loose."

"Do you want me to reward you with some pain, Harold?"

"Oh, yes, please. I like it when I'm in pain."

I'm not going to draw blood from anyone, but I don't mind slapping him around a little, giving him a teeny bit of pain, and calling him names. It might even be fun, taking my stress out on someone.

"I am your mistress and you will do as I please. Do you understand, Harold?"

"Yes. I thoroughly understand you. Yes," he nods with a look of delight but slight fear in his sky-blue eyes. "Oh, no, I've left the pegs in my carrier bag."

I lift his plastic carrier bag off the floor and take out six wooden pegs and his dildo, resting them on the bedside cabinet.

"Put them on my nipples, please, Cat."

"That's what I plan to do."

"Oh. Oh, that feels good." The pegs are doing their job, making him erect, up and running, no longer fat and floppy.

I tease him at first by sticking my tongue out before getting to work rubbing his bell-end, then sliding my hand vertically down his shaft.

"No, Cat, slow down, I'll come straight away if you do that."

"I'm in control here." I squeeze his left nipple tighter with a peg. "Does it make you horny when I squeeze your nipples hard like this? You like pain, don't you?" I'm jostling him hard and fast with the lube, now easing off the peg clasping slightly, sensing he's going to tip over the edge. Oops. He does. That was rather fast.

"Oh! Oh, yes! Yes! Yes! Yes! How lovely," he rests his head back onto a pillow, still tied down. "You're a lovely girl."

"Thank you, Harold." No need for domination now.

"I loved every minute of that. I didn't want to come so soon, but we got carried away, didn't we?"

"You can come twice in an hour, Harold. Do you know?" Most regular parlour clients know this anyway. I untie him so he can wash.

"Oh, thank you, Cat. Marvellous." He smiles as he cleans himself. "We have made a bit of a mess. It was worth it though. Ha. Ha."

"Would you like a massage, Harold? I can relax you and give you a break."

"Oh, yes, that would be lovely." Harold rolls over onto his stomach and closes his eyes. I peer at the time on the digital clock whilst I give him a back massage. The time is eleven twenty-five in the morning, approaching halfway through our one-hour service.

"I also carry out some added extras in my service."

"And what would those be?"

"I do reverse anal."

"Oh, yes, please."

Grasping the opportunity to get more money off him, I turn him over and rope him down again, tying up his ankles and wrists. Teasingly, I strip down in slow motion, hypnotising him. He watches me quietly but intently, becoming solid for a second time.

"Oh, yes, nice breasts. I wish I could feel them, but my arms are tied." He laughs.

"I'll let you touch them after I've made you come again. I'm going to tease your arse first. Do you like the sound of that, you dirty man?" Sustaining full eye contact, I want him to get lost in the sensation. I want to make him shatter into pieces again, exploding as I play with his arse. I kneel up between his spread legs, naked, facing him. He has full view of my breasts.

I slowly push the dildo in. His hard-on begins to move up and down, swaying at the movement inside him. Slowly, slowly I tease him, rubbing the dildo over his G-spot in an insistent rhythm.

"Marvellous. Oh. Oh. Oh, yes." He moans. He's causing a racket in my bedchamber.

Grabbing my lubricant, I squeeze it all over his hard-on with my left hand. I can feel him throbbing with excitement. I use my right hand to slide the dildo back and forth and my left hand to tease him.

"Oh yes. I love. . . I'm about to. . . Oh, yes, I am about to. . ." He doesn't have time to finish his sentence.

Afterwards, he says, "Would you let me take you out for dinner sometime?"

"Sorry, I have a boyfriend." Usual excuse.

The next client doesn't want sex. He giggles like a child opening his presents on Christmas morning. "I only want you to play with me, please. Tickle me. Roll around with me." I name him Roly Poly Man. Sounds fun. "Yes, we can play together." I don't think this is absurd. Others want a slap, but he wants a tickle, just like the millionaire who only ever wanted me to tickle him. Roly Poly Man needs some sort of touchy feely comfort from a woman, and this is quite normal. All men and women find pleasure in different types of comfort. I know I do.

"You don't need to take off your bra. You're fine as you are. Come here. Hug me. Tickle me. I'd like to roll with you on the bed. Can we roll over each other? I promise I won't hurt you, sweetheart," he begs, with needy, puppy-dog eyes.

"You smell wonderful." He kisses my cheeks and kisses above my breasts while I lie next to him. What could be more fun for a man than rolling around in bed with a sexy female in her panties?

"Can I take some of this in front of you?" He holds up a bottle of poppers.

"Yes, darling, of course." He sniffs up the strong glue-like substance through his left nostril and then feeds some to his right nostril, as the Bonfire Night fireworks start banging in the sky outside. Bang. Crackle. Whizz. Bang. The feral colonies will be afraid tonight. I hope they find somewhere to hide and stay safe.

Roly Poly Man rolls over me, keeping his arms around my waist. He's hard; I feel the hardness pressing up against my lingerie through his boxer shorts. He's a cuddly sort of man, nuzzling and gripping my body, but I'm wondering why he doesn't want me naked, why he doesn't want sex.

"I have no friends. Will you be my friend?" Stopping rolling, he pushes me away to survey my response.

"I'll be your friend. Yes." Maybe he's not been offered an invite to a bonfire. I guess I'm lucky in that respect because I'm going to a fireworks show later tonight.

He pulls me back towards him and hugs me tighter this

time. I put my arms around his neck and he places his around my waist. We roll up and down the divan three times. I can't control a fit of laughter coming over me, and he chuckles too.

"I love this. Do you?" he asks.

"Yes. I love it. This rolling is therapeutic."

"Oh, gosh, is that the time? I best get dressed and go, Cat. Can I see you next week?"

CHAPTER FOURTEEN

The receptionist screeches, "Cat, beautiful! Jeramiah (I know him as Dolce Boy) has gone upstairs to your room. He wants you to take a can of pop up for him."

Dolce has deep, dark, coffee-coloured, seductive eyes. He tastes like candy in my mouth. Sweet Dolce. His charm is overpowering at times. He always makes an epic entrance, swaggering as though he's on a catwalk, demanding to be noticed.

"We don't need to fuck each other to get close, I prefer to use our time by kissing and searching deep into your thoughts," he says—every time. Only each time he sees me we always end up fucking, as he is never able to keep his hands off me.

He begins kissing me uncontrollably the moment I walk in. I pull away from him slightly to close the door behind us.

"Where have you been? I've not seen your name on the rota for a little while?"

"Nowhere interesting." I play hard to get, retreating from his kisses now and then.

"Hey, don't tease." He grips my face passionately and gently bites my neck.

Running my fingertips across his body, I caress his skin whilst softly trailing kisses down his neck and spine.

"It drives me mental when you do that." He kisses my lips. He has one hell of a tantalising kiss. "Cat, I want to tell you something. You don't need to work here. I'll support you financially."

"Don't be silly. I enjoy working here."

"How much do you earn here?"

"That's personal."

"I'll match whatever you earn."

"Err, it's like most people's monthly wage, every week."

"You what? I can't beat that."

How can he support me when he has a wife and two children? He doesn't have one ounce of love for his wife, or so he tells me. She's his cousin and their marriage was arranged when they were young children. I won't be any man's second wife—not me. Besides, how could I possibly live with myself, knowing I've split a family up? I've not been brought up that way.

There were no psychological reasons for me starting this kind of work, no personal trauma. I didn't have a bad upbringing. Wasn't on drugs or drink. I was exposed to lots of different religions when I was growing up, which was a real reflection on multicultural Britain that left me quite open and relaxed with the world, not having to follow a certain religious path and not being judgemental. I went to church every Sunday as a young girl with mum and Kitty.

My grandmother brought me up with Buddhism; she was Chinese and she used to have me praying to the Buddha with strong-smelling incense sticks and the lights dimmed. I was only young, but I sensed it was her way of worshipping. My mother's father is of Pakistani origin, so Mum would dress in Muslim attire, especially around my eldest brother's father. Short skirts were worn less around them, and I was taught about the Quran. I learnt about Muslim culture and ate halal by my mother's side. When I was in my mid-teens, my auntie got me into the Methodist Church, where I got tears in my eyes at the stories they told. The church staff took me to one side and splashed some water on my head during their prayers, and I was classed as a born-again Christian after this. I remember my auntie tithing her income to the church. She used to talk in tongues to me when I was younger. "Bambada shambada. Be good," she would say when she thought I was being naughty, although I always thought I was a good girl.

"I shove a pillow over my wife's face while I'm fucking her and think of you."

"Seriously?"

"Yeah."

"That's a bit wrong."

He just laughs. "I really like you. I want to be with you. Not her."

"She's your wife, though."

"I. Want. You!" He pinches my chin firmly, raising it.

"No, you don't. It's the chase you enjoy."

"I'm being serious. I'd leave her for you. I'm only with her because of the kids. She's good to me. She cooks, cleans, and looks after my children. She's done nothing wrong, she's just not what I want. I only married her for my family. They brought her over from Pakistan to marry me. Let me take you out. Can I?"

"No," I chuckle.

"Come on, give me a try." He grabs my midriff. "Don't be shy, give me a try."

"I'm not shy and I'm not playing games and I'm definitely not playing hard to get. It's my job. I've told you before." I huff. Fucking hell. I come here to work, to get money for my business ambitions and the cats, not to be forced into dating.

"But, Cat, I love you." Damn, I've made him fall for me. He claims he loves me, but how can he? Why does this frigging job have to be so seductive?

"Love is a strong word," I kiss him lightly.

He clutches my legs, gliding my thong down, pulling my legs apart. "I've never once gone down on a girl. In. My. Life."

What? He's thirty-three years old, how can this be? I'm sure most men his age have given oral to a girl before—if they're heterosexual.

But he seems a little distracted. "Been on the vodka again. Drinking it in my car." He has no shame. "I'd have brought some in for you but it's banned in here, isn't' it?" Nobody can possibly tame him and he wouldn't listen anyhow.

"Yes, it's banned."

He's definitely drunk and unpredictably wild, throwing his face side-to-side and rubbing his stubbly chin on my sex—for god's sake; I'll get stubble rash.

"Can we get down to business now or what?"

"Let's do it without a condom on. Please! I won't squirt inside you."

"No way! Are you for real? Look, you've had a drink. You need to calm down."

"Come on, it'll feel good."

"Don't disrespect me. I don't let anyone have me without protection."

There's no way I'm consenting to him having me unprotected; the battle would be violent if he tried. Although he's strong and muscular, I'd put up a decent fight. All I'd have to do is grip his balls and squeeze them with all of my might, then run out, but I'm not missing out on my money from him. The cash I'm going to earn from Dolce will be more than a day's wage for most people.

"I'm sorry, Cat, don't fall out with me, I was just joking."

Reaching for my condom bag I watch his drunken movements as he begins to dance naked in the mirror. I open one packet with my teeth, fixated on his eyes. He's calmer now as we start kissing again. I put the condom on him. He's raring to go. He clambers on top of me. My legs wrap around his back and he deepens between my thighs. He pounds me and his erection becomes harder as he slides in and out. I like it.

"I want you to be my wife. Marry me. You can come and live with me, in my house."

He grips my neck, throttling lightly. He actually believes I'll be okey dokey with being his wife number two, or perhaps wife three or four.

"I told you. I love you. *Unconditionally.* You motherfucker, Cat. Why won't you listen to me?"

I don't appreciate being sworn at, especially in the middle of sex. It's a turn-off. I'm no motherfucker. Swearing is only acceptable to me if it's being called a 'sexy bitch' or a 'randy bitch' or 'dirty slut'.

"Right. That's it. Your time's up now."

"Wait. I need to come. Lick my nipples, tell me you love me, and lick my balls." Nipples, I love you, then balls. This always makes him climax. So, nipples, I love you, then balls is what I'll do.

"Wait," he says. "Can you go to reception and see if I can have you for another half hour? I'll wait here while you go and check."

Hmmm. More money? Yes indeed. I wrap a towel around my naked body.

"Can the guy in my room have me for an extra thirty minutes?"

"Yes, you've had a cancellation. See if you can try and get him to have a two-girl with you. Erin's free."

"Good idea." Maybe this is what I need to do when I open my own brothel, doubling the money by sending two girls in to one booking, because it's easier to get extra money out of organising a threesome. "Erin, stand by while I try to tempt this guy into having some extra fun."

"Great." Erin claps excitedly as I go back in.

"My friend wants to come in the room with us for some fun. You'll have to pay her extra for her time."

"I only want to share my time with you, not another girl."

Damn. Erin's desperate for this money or she won't make enough to pay her reception fee at the end of the day. (Anyone who works here has to pay a fee to the reception, depending on how many clients she sees. This place has a business to run so as well as the guys paying, the ladies do too. Some call it a tip which goes to the cleaner and the receptionist, tallying up their wage.) Plus, Erin has just come back from Ibiza. Holidaying and wild partying habits are her thing so

I'm guessing she could do with the money. She's the type of girl who enjoys cocaine and vodka nights out. The majority of her bookings are walk-ins, no reservations, no guaranteed clients and no guaranteed money.

'Erin's the type of girl who rushes men into ending the service quicker than expected, so I wouldn't bother if I were you. A typical hand job queen. No kissing. No GFE. She cared more about the way she looked, looking in the mirror at herself, than looking at me.' That was one of her online reviews.

If Dolce allows Erin in the boudoir with us, it'll be on my terms, not hers. Most of my clientele have the opportunity to spend their full time with me. If I can make them return, it proves they were pleased, and then I, in turn, can bring in more cash.

"Go on," stroking his leg. "It'll be fun. Be adventurous. Have you never had two girls in the bedroom at once? Are you scared? You can watch her and me together. I can lick her nipples and she can go down on me in front of you. We can lick your nipples together. It'll turn you on."

"If you want her in the room," he pauses, "go and get her."

"Give me the reception fee for Erin and I'll take it down then bring her back up with me."

Erin is still waiting on a leather seat at the reception desk. None of us like to be waiting, twiddling our thumbs. Everyone would much prefer to be on their backs, client atop them, or bent over, or whatever it is they're being paid to do.

"Let's go have some fun," I link Erin's arm and head back towards Dolce. "Dolce, this is Erin. Erin, this is Dolce. Let's fuck. Who do you want first?" Pretending I'm unsure of his answer.

"Need you ask?" he reacts sarcastically.

Erin's eyes roll back. Oh shit!

"Do you want to see some girl-on-girl action?" I ask.

"As you please."

"It's a little extra." I throw my towel onto the tiled floor.

"You know I don't mind about the money."

Erin strips so she's topless. Her fake E cups are the sort any guy would love to touch. I begin stroking her nipples. I touch myself, and there's a moist feel, and so I edge myself onto him, back off, on again. Not taking in his full length, just the tip, teasing him.

"Give it to me, baby. Fucking fuck me. Like you want to." He touches my body firmly, wanting me, craving me.

I turn to face the wall mirror. "Watch it. . . can you see it. . . sliding. . . in and out of me?" Trying to turn him on more. His dick is becoming even more rock hard. "Let's swap now. Erin hasn't felt you inside her yet." I pass Erin a fresh condom. She places it skilfully over his dick with her lips whilst pulling her fluorescent, plaited, green bikini briefs off. I work my way down his toned legs, showering him with kisses whilst Erin sits atop. Now at his balls, I roll my tongue all over them.

"Cat, I want you to fuck me."

I peer up from licking his balls and all I can view is Erin's naked back, not moving. I bet she's proper pissed off at him not wanting her on top of him. I crawl up the side of his body, on all fours, resembling a lioness out on the prowl, eyes powerfully on my prey. He's not one bit interested in Erin. I shouldn't have recommended her, or any other girl to share this booking to be frank. He's making it clear he only wants me, making things uncomfortable.

"Hey, you've gone soft." Erin is in shock. She lifts her body off him, with both palms up in the air, not knowing what to do. She'd better not start causing a commotion. I don't want my client unsettled. She could at least follow my lead, kiss his neck, touch him, do something, anything—she's being paid, after all.

"Leave it to me," I say. "You want to watch girl-on-girl? Want me caressing Erin?" I run the soft tips of my acrylic fingernails in motions around Erin's cleavage, luring him.

"Go ahead."

The more I touch her, whilst touching him, the more his body trembles. I tempt and tease. Tempt and tease. I flicker my tongue on her nipple and suckle it and look into his eyes. I kiss Erin's lips then make my way back to her nipple. We're both naked, kneeling on the divan. She seems a little edgy, but she doesn't need to be jittery around me. I can be the leading female if that's what she wants—lay her down, lick her sex, give her an orgasm.

"Join in," I offer him to Erin, slanting his hard-on to the left. After all, I can't leave her out, it's a threesome for God's sake. We take turns, sucking him. Up, off, down. Swap. Slow, fast, breathe. Swap. Tip, whole length, deep throat. Up, down, up, down. Breathe. Swap. I'm getting turned on at his moans.

"Wait! Stop. Can't take any more. Too much." Too much for him? I haven't even started. "I'll watch you two get it on with each other again. Get between her legs."

"Yes, sir." Smirking, doing as I'm told, giving him the I-want-you-to-fuck-me eyes.

I circle my tongue on her clit.

"Finger her." Dolce's head raises, making sure I'm delivering.

I lick three fingers, taking it slowly. "Like this?" My index finger is lost inside her. She moans. The faster I finger, the more she moans. Men must love making girls moan, dishing out pleasure like this.

"Fuck, yeah." He slaps his hard-on.

"Give it to me from behind, while I go down on her." I take charge. I uncover my face, moving my hair so it doesn't block his view. I want him to see it all.

"I. . . I . . . Stop. Sorry."

"Everything okay?" I turn round to face him.

"That's the thing. It's too fucking good." He holds his hand on his forehead. "You lick her and I'll take a break."

I lay down, widening my legs on the couch, letting her do as she pleases with me. It doesn't faze me; she can either carry out the real deal or fake the fantasy. Whoa, she's not afraid, plunging her face right between my thighs. I whine as she tongues my sex again and again, sucking lightly on my clit. I don't mind her going down on me right now, her tongue's unbelievably soft and warm, licking in the right place. I let loose on a flowing orgasm. It's unusual for a woman to give me an orgasm.

Having got what I wanted out of this threesome I ask, "How can we both make you finish off, Dolce?"

"It won't take long. I want to be sucked off."

"Fine. You're aware of the price for come-in-mouth aren't you, darling?"

"Yes."

"So, you want me sucking you until you explode in my wet mouth?" I get on my knees in front of him and pull Erin's naked body towards me so she can take turns next. He stands on the divan, putting his hand on the mirrored ceiling above the bed. I tug him slowly, back and forth, picking up the pace, a little faster, a little faster, back and forth, back and forth, kissing and licking his balls. Then I begin to suck him.

"Yes, suck it. Suck it faster, motherfucker." Right, so now he's swearing at me again. "Slag, Erin, lick my balls."

Licking a finger and thumb, I toy with his nipples whilst deep throating.

"Fucking hell, you're really hitting the spot now. Tell me you love me." Here goes—nipples, I love you, then balls.

"Dolce, I love you." I take a breath from sucking. "Taste it," I order Erin.

"I sure will." She takes her turn.

Dolce gazes at me. "Cat, finish me off. Where do you want it?"

"On my face." I want the extra money from the speciality of COF.

"I'm nearly there."

I bite my bottom lip gently. Taking hold of Erin's arm, I pull her towards my side. I lick my finger and play with his right nipple, then his left nipple, then I tickle his balls whilst tugging him with my other hand, going all out. I pull hard on his nipples.

"Ahh, baby! Ahh. I'm going to. . ."

Here goes. We both position our faces in wait. He lets loose. "Amazing. Thanks."

"I'm glad you liked it, darling." I wink at Erin and jump in the shower.

"That was fun, Dolce." The warm water flows over my naked body. I'd have had to slog for this money in a normal job.

In the changing room, Erin is applying lipstick in the mirror. Her face tells me everything.

"He's persistent with me, as you can see, but you needed the money."

"He made me uncomfortable, that's all. I know it isn't your fault."

"Aww, babe, I'm sorry, I didn't expect him to be rude with you. We've never had another person in the room with us before."

"Things aren't going my way today, that's all. I'm feeling a bit down."

"I've been feeling a bit down lately, too."

"Australia," she says. "There's loads of places there, high-class places like Platinum Heels. If you want to earn loads of cash where nobody knows you."

Her words turn a light on in my head. Platinum Heels is a renowned short-stay boutique hotel and brothel. I could do with a bit of a holiday. The world is a big place, and it could all be my oyster, if I so choose.

The next day I reach for my laptop, realising I need to get the ball rolling. I need to apply to this so-called Platinum Heels in Australia. Browsing through the sumptuous suites on their website I make a decision—yeah, this is definitely where I'd like to be.

Dear Platinum Heels

I've heard many exciting stories about your place and wondered whether you would allow me to work for you.

A little about me: I have flawless skin with deep chocolate eyes and a curvy toned figure with long legs and plump breasts. Men just can't help but want to come back for more after I've serviced them. I specialise in GFE, unless the client prefers domination. I am a very versatile lady, making each of my clients my number one priority.

I've attached three professional pictures of myself for your attention. I am working at one of the finest parlours in England and have built an excellent reputation for myself. I aim to please in every aspect of my job and this shines through with my repeat customers.

I look forward to hearing from you. It would be a pleasure to work at Platinum Heels. I am thinking of staying in Sydney for three weeks.
Kind regards,
Cat

If Platinum Heels doesn't accept me, I'm sure there are plenty of other places over there, but let's just see.

"The girls always want me in their room." Cynthia, my escort friend, has just started at a local massage parlour as she has been struggling to get by, but wants to finish her nurse training and get her qualification. She's been doing out-call bookings for the past few years here and there, and that's a godsend to her. I got her into escorting because I saw her struggling to put food on the table. It's a way out of poverty.

She continues, "I think it's fun when the girls are in the room with clients too. Most of my shifts I'd do threesomes. Love it. I'm quite good at domination."

"Really?" I snicker, but we're in the local carvery pub and I see the couple beside us rudely staring our way. Eek, maybe they heard what she said.

I'm a private person so I begin to whisper, but her voice seems a lot louder than mine. I've come for a meal with her because she's always saying how I never make time for friends as I'm always busy with the cats, and I understand totally; these cats take over my life. I haven't even had time to put make-up on today or brush the knots out of my hair. I always used to make sure I left the house fully made up, with perfume on, looking and feeling immaculate, but anyone in rescue will probably understand why I wish there were more hours in the day. It is lovely to catch up with friends. I should be getting my nails done like I used to, but nowadays it hurts too much when my false acrylics get caught in the cat traps and rip off, so I leave them natural and don't even bother with varnish, as I'm always washing cat bowls and then washing my hands, so it never lasts.

"There's this guy who came to see me and he's like 'spit in my mouth' and so I do it and call him a dirty fucking bastard and tell him he's lucky I'm not asking him to pay extra for it. So, he said, 'let me spit it back in your mouth,' and I slapped him across the face." Her hands come forward with the slapping motion near my face. I throw my body back in the chair and we both fall about in stitches. I look back at the couple and they are sure as hell watching and listening. Jeez.

"You're so funny."

"Yeah, I told him how dare he ask me to take that spit back. I told him to get into the shower and let me piss all over him, and I said he'd be giving me the extra money. The girls buzz off me in there."

I know others survive off a low wage packet, but I suppose once you've had the money a call-girl gets, the cost of living can also go up. With me, it's shopping for cat food and for her it's always new clothes and holidays. She does want to settle down and I believe she would stop work if Mr Right came along. Just because a girl does this kind of work doesn't make her a bad person.

"What you up to for the rest of the day? Cat stuff?" She knows me too well.

"I've just fed the barn cats colony." She's helped me feed them before and trap two of them; she knows how much I care about them all. "And I've been to pick up some parcels. One is some cat food off a lovely friend and a cloth cat cone for Beauty, the feral girl who needs her ruptured eye out. I'm dreading putting that cone on her, but my cat friend was so lovely to buy it. Before I met you I went to meet my cousin and helped her catch a cat that was hiding under a cabinet from some domestic violence case. Then I'll be going home, sorting the garage cats colony out and feeding my lot at home. It's never ending."

"How do you get by? Do you just live off donations?"

"No, the donations don't even cover the cost of what the cats cost to feed. I do competitions on the cats' social media to raise funds and things like that, but I don't really like asking people for money. Sometimes I do fundraisers to help with vet bills, but it does cost me hundreds a week."

"Wow, I don't know how you afford it. The people at the stables ['stables' is our code word for the parlour she rides in] say it's busier at night there and that I should work evenings, but that means I'll have to pay more of a house fee."

"Yeah, but it would be worth it."

That's the thing—it's always worth it. Or is it? If I don't

work, I'm worrying, big time. The cats rely on me. If I do work, I'm worrying big time that people may suss me out. Maybe I'll have a go at a 'real world' job.

I've been seeing more and more of my 'real-world' boyfriend lately too. I've been trying to put him into the back of my mind because people say you can't have a boyfriend in this line of work, and I want to keep him. I call him Mr Gold. He doesn't know about my job.

*

A deep cerise rose nestles in a glass vase. We've had a romantic, candlelit dinner at Mr Gold's. Staring into his eyes, my love for him starts to deepen. But maybe his love is going to suffocate me by stopping me from working. I wonder if it'll ruin us.

"What's wrong?" he asks.

"Nothing, babe, nothing whatsoever. I've had a long day, that's all. I'm a little tired. Nothing some wine won't cure." I toast him with my glass and cheekily stick my tongue out.

As I reach to take our half-full wine glasses away Gold picks me up, carrying me into his lounge and seating me on his crushed velvet sofa.

"I'm thirsty for you." He rests his hands on my head, fisting my hair together, pulling me to his face and biting my bottom lip. I love this. It's not the kissing I long for. It's his 'I'm-in-charge-of-you' approach. My hair still clasped in his palm, he sends my head downwards, my knees automatically giving way. I do as he pleases, unbuttoning him. He grows hard in my mouth. I ripple my warm tongue down him, and then encase him in the tightness of my lips. In rhythmic motions, I deep-throat.

"That's it, you little bitch, suck on it." He's filthy, wiping his hard-on over my cheeks and nose, then slapping it over my lips. He tilts my head to the left, still gripping a fistful of my hair, trailing two of his fingers up and down my tongue. Gently, despite his masculine power, he clutches my hips, controlling me, lifting me up towards him as he nibbles my neck on the sofa. Hot flushes wave across my body as he lifts my vest over my shoulders to reveal my bra. I let him know I want him by drawing my leggings down from my hips to my ankles, throwing them aside, pulling at the edges of my knickers, looking in his eyes the entire time.

"No. Allow me." He prefers to take my knickers off himself.

Parting my legs for him, laying back, I yearn for him to be inside me. As I unclasp the back of my bra, he drops my knickers on top of my breasts and leaves them there. I don't know why he does this. No man has ever draped my panties over my naked body before. There's something I like about it.

"Kiss me." I raise my body. His lips are mine. Only mine.

"Where?" He's brazen as he lowers his face, kissing me below. He's in control. He undresses fully and throws me down so I'm lying on my back, rubbing his body up towards my breasts, yanking on my hair, kissing my face then lightly biting, showing his authority. He rules me.

"Oh," I jump a little as his tongue tickles me, trailing down the sides of my sex, and back up, causing unexpected spasms. "Baby." I gently clasp his head with my nails, digging into his scalp. 'Stop." Why do I say stop? "That's going to make me orgasm."

"And?" he pauses, "would that be a bad thing?"

I smile naughtily. He knows I want him to carry on. Picking up where he left off. Damn, his tongue. . .

"Baby," I moan as I flush with hot sweats, "that's turning me on." I hold on to his powerful arms. "Baby." His tongue is faster now. "Damn." I'm shaking.

"Don't hold back," he growls.

"God, I fucking love your tongue." Breathing heavily, "I'm so wet, so hot. And I'm so fucking horny right now."

He carries on with his tongue, pushing a finger in, and my whole body shakes with an orgasm. He works his way up to my face, kissing me softly up my stomach, biting my nipple lightly, and then kisses my neck as he deepens into me. I moan in pleasure.

"Take it, baby," he says in my ear.

"Baby."

"Don't fight it."

"You're making me feel like I'm going to. . ." I squeeze his butt cheeks, pulling his body into me as my legs rise higher.

"Going to what?"

"You know what."

"What?"

"Fuck. Harder."

"Tell me what I'm going to make you do?"

"Come," I pant, as he builds up his momentum.

"Do it. Come for me again, sexy bitch," he growls.

"I want you inside me."

We share tongues, as he carries on pounding me from above. He begins to run his tongue around my nipples, one by one, looking in my eyes then looking back down at my breasts, wetting my nipples, and then blowing on them one by one. He looks into my eyes, into my soul, and then looks down at my breasts again and traces his tongue over my nipples, then back at me, repeating, stimulating me over and over as I watch him. His eyes tell me to watch him licking. He kisses my forehead whilst pushing in and out, harder and then more gently, harder and then more gently. I dig my fingers into his arms as he pounds me faster and deeper and harder, and before I know it, we're in another room making love on his carpet.

"You're mine. This is mine." He snaps and points in between my legs.

He wants me all to himself. I feel he has his suspicions—there are rumours about me in our neighbourhood—but I've denied them because I don't want to be judged.

"Yes, you're right, all yours. Nobody else's."

He cups my breasts from behind, then traces his fingertips down my spine.

"I'm going to spank your backside." He slaps me hard.

"I like you spanking me."

"Dirty slut."

"Harder." I want all of him. I grip the carpet and push back on him.

"Can't take much more of this. You want my come?" He rests his palms around my waist then strokes my hips as he rocks and plunges into me.

"Yes. All of it."

"Fuck. I'm going to come." I feel every inch.

I scream in pleasure as he releases into me.

*

Later, I check my emails.

Assistant Sales Manager. Haberdashery store. £17,000 per annum—No.

Store Manager. Card shop. Full-time. 47.5 hours per week—No.

Department manager. Womenswear. Clothes store. 36 hours per week—Possibly.

Unfortunately, you have not been successful in your application.

Flipping great, I'm getting rejected from the normal jobs I'm applying for. Next email.

I am pleased to inform you that the first stage of your application has been successful, and we would like to invite you to attend the second stage of the selection process. We look forward to hearing from you.

I must reply and show interest, even though I can't imagine living on such a low salary. Maybe if I can show Mr Gold that I can hold down a normal job, things will work out. I tell him about it the next time I'm round his.

"I've been applying for jobs."

"What type of jobs?" He raises a sceptical eyebrow. Gosh, what does he take me for? I used to have a normal job. I can work a normal job again if I so please.

"Retail jobs, you know."

"And?"

"And I've got a response. I've phoned them up and arranged to have a face-to-face interview tomorrow morning. Can you believe it? That quick."

"That's great, baby," he kisses me on my forehead.

"It's to be a department manager in a store. I need to get revising." I walk off to grab a pen and paper from his office.

I read out loud, "Managing the profit and loss of the store. Devising and executing strategic plans with regards to performance. Driving a team to maximise sales and KPI targets set. Frequently reviewing all members of staff, including management, in probationary periods and annually. Managing stock levels and making key decisions about stock control. Analysing sales figures and forecasting future sales to maximise profits. Managing, recruiting, motivating, training and developing sales team to increase sales." I remember my duties from when I was a manager, even though it was a while ago.

"Sounds impressive, baby." He strokes my hair as he walks by.

"Memorising isn't easy."

"Carry on. You can do this."

"I can't memorise it all, it's too much," I complain.

"There's no such thing as can't."

"Yes, there is."

"We don't do can't in this house."

"Stop distracting me then, sexy arse."

"If you stop reading, I'll bend you over and spank you."

"Oh, and that's meant to be a threat, is it? Say stuff like that to me and I'll jump on you."

"Later, this is important."

"Fine," I carry on. "Delivering and motivating staff in excellent customer service at all times, managing and assessing HR issues. Maintaining store and visual merchandising standards to the highest levels. Ensuring excellent product knowledge in order to drive sales and deliver customer satisfaction."

The next day, on my way to the interview, I'm repeating it all in my mind, traipsing past the pollution-covered tower blocks, walking up the cobbled street. It's awkward to walk straight over these cobbles in heels. Passers-by, mostly men, can't take their eyes off me, like vultures circling, ready to swoop on me, their prey. Talons out, ready to latch on, de-feather me. Hunters. I'm uncomfortable walking through this much people-traffic, sensing that some may know me from work.

In fact, the passers-by probably don't know me from Eve. It seems the parlour has traumatised me, yet I already miss being there. I miss the fun, miss the sex, miss the socialising, miss my friends there, miss the money, and it's only been a few days of trying to be more in the 'real world'.

I blow the interviewer away with my confidence and previous management experience. She takes a liking to my handbag, not knowing I purchased it through selling my body, and offers me the job, starting the next day. Without thinking properly, I take the offer. I suppose I do it to please my beau only—it's not to please me. I'm not looking forward to my new, underpaid job one bit, but I have to prove I'm not a bad egg, show I'm capable of being a worthy girlfriend and prevent any gossip. Am I trying to convince other people, or myself? Kitty will be fine for a little while now I've given her some money to support her studies.

At five in the morning, I wake up to start my 'real world' shift at eight-thirty. This is early for me. My blood is boiling at my alarm going off at this godforsaken time. Five in the fucking morning! I envy him; he's allowed to remain asleep as he works for himself. No time schedules for him. I apply makeup in his en suite. I'm tired. Switching on the walk-in wardrobe spotlights, eyes not ready for the brightness, I search through my three wardrobes for a suit. I must appear presentable. No need for stockings, sussies or stilettos today. I grab a pink lace thong and a black push-up padded support bra—un-matching underwear. I wouldn't dream of wearing underwear that didn't match in my sex-work job, but nobody is seeing what's under my clothes now. I open a small gap in the curtains but sunrise hasn't even touched the leaded windows. A world of darkness awaits me.

The suit skirt I select is mid-length, pale beige in colour, with a matching jacket and white shirt. No time for ironing, plus I'm not in the mood, I haven't got the energy. I'd probably singe the shirt collar. Suit on, pat the creases out. Put my feet into short-heeled, patent leather shoes—makes a change from stilettos.

Crawling across Mr Gold's four-poster bed, over the heavy tog blanket, I kiss him lightly on the lips. He opens his eyes.

"Have a nice day, beautiful." He seems relaxed, content with my new-found work ethic.

"See you later." Through gritted teeth. Yeah, stay bed-bound, while I wake to join the rat race, catching the tram in the darkness, all on my own. Anyone could get me. I park my car at the station car park then walk up the concrete staircase to the platform. Discarded newspapers are blowing like mini whirlwinds. I walk side to side, avoiding spots of tacky bubble gum. A cigarette remnant sticks to my sole, so I scrape my shoe along the platform. Normally, I would throw my shoes away if they were scraped, I'd just get a new pair, but now I haven't the money to waste. I have to be careful with what I have left.

Screech. The train arrives. I'm thrown side-to-side on my feet for thirty minutes or so, juggling my handbag, phone and empty diary, holding on to the strap for dear life.

"Sorry, love." A strange man elbows my boob. Ouch! Thanks a bunch. Probably not a mistake. Pervert.

There's not much space, so why are twenty more passengers squeezing in? Ouch, my flipping foot. I couldn't be more pissed off right now. I can't imagine putting up with this journey twice a day, there and back, five days a week. I'd much rather be cruising comfortably through the city centre in my sporty car, leaning back, showing off, feeling proud and independent that I'm making money—and lots of it, at that. Barging through the sardines, I wrestle my way off the crammed, overflowing train.

Mr Gold messages:

Really proud of you, my beauty. I really am. X

I reply:

Proud of me. Oh, okay. x

I feel the opposite, not proud of myself for quitting the Palace Lounge, and unable to hide my resentment.

Yes, you are trying hard, I know you are, and it is an honest job. Love you. x

The city streets are chaotic. Everyone is travelling to work in a rush, banging past me, no one apologising, no one saying sorry for battering their holdalls into my legs or standing on my shoes. The weather is a grim shower and my dampened hair is beginning to frizz from roots to tips, split-ends showing—fucking great.

Is this the new life I want? No, not at all. What should I do then? I could be warm in my old workplace, strutting around, flaunting my libido in flimsy underwear, having cash thrown at me, fulfilling my sex addiction and getting paid for it, but I'm trying to live a different life. I picture the women I used to work alongside at the Palace Lounge and frown at the money they'll earn today and the pleasure they'll receive, envying them. But I've got myself in this predicament. I'm the one who quit. No one else is to blame.

Four weeks later, my eyes have distinct dark circles around them. I despise my new job. There's too much to absorb and heaps of responsibility to handle. I'm fine with my time-management skills, and know how to do this job, but I'm not giving it my all because I don't belong here. I'm walking in someone else's shoes, living someone else's life.

I've become pally with my new retail colleagues. They're nice, but my new boss Ms Blackwell, I'll refer to her as Blackwell, is a complete asshole, constantly on a power trip and clearly aiming to ruin our lives. She's already made three members of the team quit. Louisa, my new friend on womenswear cries to me in the staff room every time she has been screamed at by Blackwell. I wonder if she'll see how hard-working I can be and take a shine to me.

I've just caught Blackwell staring at me from behind the adjacent étagère display cabinet. Seeing I've noticed her spying she steps forward, eyeing me up and down, trying to intimidate me, wanting to assert her authoritative presence. She has a distinctive dark mole on her left cheek, and chin-length, bobbed, straw-like hair. No one dares stand up to her. She charges my way.

"So, you've been here for four weeks now, haven't you? That means you're responsible for anything that goes wrong in your section." She's furious, right in my face and I don't know why. "Explain. To. Me. Why the work hadn't been completed yesterday?" Her scattered spit hits my cheek. Eww.

"Yesterday was not my shift. I don't know what work hasn't been completed. I'll find out."

"You. Should. Know. It is your job to be aware of everything in here. You. Are. Not. Challenging people on the job. You need a review." Her nostrils flare, and she turns towards the merchandising team leader, parading towards her. Take a chill-pill, you witch. I'm defenceless. She could fire me on the spot. She's the master here, the decision maker, and we all cower.

Later, when I've finished my shift, nine hours of boring, demanding slog, I'm relieved to escape. It's bland. Mind-numbing. The same thing every day. I'm not getting any satisfaction out of it. And now I'm being verbally attacked. I'm a performing poodle here, and I'm only doing it because I'm literally trying to be a better person.

When the train arrives, I squeeze in. Sweaty. Putrid. Sticky.

No seats. Gosh, my feet are swollen and sore—eleven hours of wearing high heels, including the travelling. It's six o'clock, and most people are on their way home from work. I release my shoes for a few brief seconds and notice weeping blisters are stinging the backs of my ankles and pinkie toes. What I'd pay for a seat right now. At the Palace Lounge I'd fling my heels off and pounce on the divan; I didn't get blisters there.

Glancing around, a deer in the headlights, I see an old client of mine a few steps away, recognising the beak-shaped nose that prodded my sex. He thinks he owns the front end of the train, one hand on his hip, the other on grab rail, and eyeballs in my direction. Fuck! Shit! Help! I turn my back. I can't remember his name. I've slept with that many different men. I'm sure I feel his eyeballs in the back of my head, willing me to turn back to face him. All I recall is that he'd bring a pair of eighty denier tights in, paying me to wear them for him.

He had no trouble vigorously ripping the tights in half to get to me, imagining me in his office bending over, or picturing a girl in short skirt and tights at a supermarket checkout. He even admitted crashing his car in broad daylight once, because he set eyes on a tights-wearing lady who was temptingly sticking her rear out while filling up with fuel. I have a pair of tights on today, so no doubt he's observing their sheen. He could make a move any minute now and rip them off. He's done it to me before, so he could almost certainly do it again. I can picture him slipping notes down my bra after fulfilling his fantasy.

The train halts at the next stop and passengers evacuate, leaving a few free seats. I rush to the rear of the train to claim a seat. My heart thumps. The last thing I want is for him to try it on with me in public. Please don't let him park his arse next to me. The train comes to a halt again. The tannoy announces my stop and the automatic doors slide apart. Stepping off the train, I rush to my car to escape. Turning my stereo up full blast, I drive to Mr Gold's house.

"Come here." He stretches his arms out, welcoming me. "Have you had a nice day?"

"No. I've had the worst day of my life." Shrugging off his hug, I walk into his kitchen, intending to pour myself a robust glass of something alcoholic. I need to forget the day's happenings.

"Why, baby? What's happened? Tell me."

"Blackwell, the boss... such a bitch." I search through his drinks cabinet, finding whisky. "She happily embarrassed me in front of about seven people, raising her voice at me, spittle in my face. She belittled me. I don't know how much longer I'll be able to handle this for." Sipping the whisky in my right hand then holding my head in my left hand. I'm getting a migraine—some paracetamol wouldn't go amiss.

"Try and stick it out, baby." He doesn't care. Try and stick it out? That's the last thing I need to hear right now. Why should I stick it out? My life doesn't depend on this dull job. Or does it? So much that I'm going through this stress?

"I don't want to speak about it. It's making me angry. You don't understand because you haven't had to go through what I've had to go through. You're your own boss. You wouldn't like a witch talking down to you, either." I glare at the kitchen floor, whisky in hand.

"It'll be okay. Just don't let her get to you. Try to stick it out for a little longer, so you have more experience on your CV."

His phone sounds out just in time to save him from a tongue lashing. He's unthoughtful, only caring for his own wellbeing and what others might be saying about me behind my back.

That night I don't get one ounce of rest, staring at the ceiling, headache overpowering my sleep. Before I began working as a call-girl, I was living a plain life, blind to the world. But now my eyes have been opened, now I see what my life can be—financially well-off. I've been transformed, I'm not who I was. I don't want to go back to the life I had when I worked in the lacklustre store with Priscilla on the minimum wage, living in and over my overdraft.

I want the life that I know is out there.

CHAPTER FIFTEEN

In July, my sister gets the long-awaited results of her law degree, and she's passed the honours course with a high mark. I'm over the moon for her. This is the reward for the long hours she's put in studying and me working to fund her education. All she needed was a pass, and she nearly got a First Degree Honours, very nearly. Now she can join the Bar Professional Training Course (BPTC).

But sadly, her elation doesn't last for long due to this letter.

Student finance for academic year.
First term tuition fees = £ 3,465.00
Second term tuition fees = £ 3,465.00
Third term tuition fees = £ 3,465.00
Total tuition fees = £ 10,395.00
This letter details how your student finance total is made up and when your university should expect payments.

I'm working as hard as I can to help fund the cats, pay for her travel and living expenses whilst at university, and I also have to pay back her tuition fee loan at some point. She's also about to start applying for the BPTC Masters at another university, which she tells me will be costly.

The day of Kitty's graduation dawns. Adonis definitely can't make it. I'm gutted, I wanted him to see what graduating is all about. I wanted him to get a taste for it, so he puts all his effort in when he starts college. Give him the hunger for higher education.

"Adonis has had nosebleeds all night and is obviously too exhausted to come." I tell my sister over the phone what my mum had told me.

"Not to worry," Kitty says. "Can he try?"

"I doubt he'll be able to make it at such short notice. So, I guess it's just you, me and Mum. Anyways, have you got your cap and gown ready? I'm setting off in five. I'll meet you at Mum's."

"Yes, I have everything ready. I'm nervous."

"Don't be nervous, sis'. You've waited three long years for this day, and you've worked so hard for it. I'm so proud of you."

*

I wake up to my alarm at four. Already? Flipping marvellous. I'm shattered. Yesterday was a busy day celebrating my sister's graduation. It's dreary outside and I have to be in work for seven today, so Blackwell insists, for new office preparation. This time I leave Mr Gold without a goodbye; he's not worthy, allowing me to be bullied like this. I'm not happy with him, to say the least. He shouldn't care what others say about me. My phone rings. It's him.

"Where was my kiss when you left, baby?" he grumbles down the phone.

"Oh, morning, I didn't want to wake you." I'm not telling him my true feelings. More like, "I'm thinking about leaving you, going back to the Palace Lounge and not giving a shit."

"Have a nice day and try not to let your boss get to you."

"I'll try. Nearly at work now, anyway, speak to you later."

I can't even turn to him with my worries. I have no shoulder to lean on. He doesn't understand what I'm going through; wanting me to 'stick it out'.

"Do you know where we are?" roars Blackwell. She's literally dragged me to the fifth floor.

"A stockroom."

"Have you been here before?"

"No."

"Why not?"

"No one has ever brought me here."

"Pathetic. Sad excuse." As she smacks fleece coats onto a clothes rail. Sad excuse? Fuck. Off. Who does she think she is? This time she has me alone, trying to break me down, no one to witness. "You should ask. Be more challenging on the job." Satisfaction covers her face. I'm the only manager on the floor. No learning plan set. No tick-box list left. No nothing. I'm working off my own intuition. I've been left in the lurch.

"Rachelle is off. Diane is off too. Nobody's trained me."

"I don't care. There's menswear, childrenswear, homeware and furnishings, there's beauty and cosmetics. No excuse. All floors have managers on."

What? So, I'm supposed to take them off their shop floors,

away from their time schedules, to teach me, when I haven't been formally introduced to any of them?

"I didn't know I could ask another department area to train me."

"Train, coach and develop, is what they all do. They give me more than you give me. Other managers challenge me. Why can't you?"

"In any normal circumstance the job would take four weeks training. I've not had one week's worth of training. Now I know I can go to other areas, I'll be asking other managers on other floors, but until then I'm still new to them, unfamiliar."

She changes tack. "The bikinis are to be replenished; the rails are running low. Why haven't you come to the stock room to fill up?"

"I haven't been given the passcode to any of the doors on these levels."

"The other supervisors can show you; they know."

"Okay."

"Change the perimeters of the swimwear."

"What about the merchandising strategy?'

"Do something. I don't care what, but make it look better than how it is."

She stamps her out-of-fashion heels towards the rusty elevator, not asking me to follow her lead but expecting me to anyway. Brands pay fixed prices for space on the shop floor. This department's turnover is five million annually; the clothes can be there one minute and gone the next, which is why the bikini fixtures weren't full, but anything this hag wishes will have to be—for now.

Rusty elevator rolling shutter closed. Lift shutter door sealed.

Level one selected. Pressing lift buttons is the most work I've ever seen her do.

"Staff counts for today?" She affords no eye contact, back facing me, her eyes to the shutter, cold body language. I'm not even worth looking in the eye, it seems.

"Twenty-four in-house staff, thirty-six brand house staff. I will be allocating duties of rails throughout the shop floor with both in-house and brand house employees."

That must be good enough for her, as she affords no reply. She may want me to fail on the questions asked, maybe she wants to have a reason to sack me, a case against me for dismissal. Why does she hate me so much? What have I ever done to her? She's married; I notice her wedding ring. I've probably bedded her husband. Take that.

"Take me through today." She steps out of the elevator, thinking she'll catch me off guard, but this is one thing I do know.

"Of course," I fake a smile. "Last year's sales on today are three thousand, four hundred. Today's target is four thousand two hundred and fifty. Twenty-five per cent increase. Week on week we're looking at thirty thousand rounded off last year, and sixty-two thousand rounded off for this week. Yesterday's sales were like-for-like. I've displayed the sunglasses stands at the main till-point for sales increase and add-ons."

"So, you know what you're doing?"

"Yes." Back off.

"More?" She won't give up. She has time to grill me. Perhaps she wants me to slip up.

"Twenty-eight rails are being delivered, as we speak, in the loading bay. I will be arranging for replenishment of new season stock first, then when the late shift staff arrive I will rota them in for the rest of the delivery. Changing room rails are being shipped back onto areas. I have four colleagues focusing on changing room rails and a further two on straightening up and finger-spacing the rows on each own-bought brand."

"As you were."

Point proven.

Break time. I call my mother.

"I don't know what to do, Mum. I don't know whether I should leave this job, it's a dreadful place to work."

"Leave. Don't go back in. Get on the train and don't look back. Come here."

"If I leave, will I be a failure? If I can't stick at a normal job, I'm useless. It's unbearable at times." I hold my tears in. I won't let Blackwell make me cry.

"Listen to me. You don't need that job. It's low paid, and you are not a failure."

I pause in silence, taking in her motherly advice.

"Did you hear me?"

"Yes, I heard. I'm outside on my break. I might go back in and see if I can get through the day."

"No. Don't. You're making a massive mistake. Your misery is only going to get worse."

"All my stuff is in my locker, though. I'll call you later, Mum. Love you. Thanks for being there for me."

"Empty your locker and come to my house. I mean it. You don't need this job. You can go back to your old job."

She's right, I know she is, but keeping this 'real world' job might save my relationship with Mr Gold. At the moment I can actually talk to him in the evening about what I've done during the day. I don't have to be making things up and staying on my guard all the time in case I slip up with my story.

Disorientated, I open my locker. I'm the only one in the dark locker room. There's nobody to make me stay. Peeking over my shoulder I see there is nobody behind me. Nobody would care if I left, nobody would stop me. But if I quit it doesn't speak volumes for my CV. But why am I even working here? Why do I stay? All I get from this job is a shit wage, lip from Blackwell and a touch of respect from Mr Gold. I turn back to my locker. A pair of kitten heels, a pair of flat shoes, my blazer, a bottle of perfume and my 'real world' work diary.

Taking the plunge, I gather all my belongings. I won't be spoken to disrespectfully ever again, by Blackwell, or anyone. Screw anyone who wants to talk down to me. I don't know how my life will pan out, but I'm going back to call girl work.

*

It's the middle of winter and it's so cold that there's a thin layer of ice on the bins outside at the barn cats colony. If you were to put your hand on that bin it would sting. The winter sun isn't hot, but many of the cats have huddled together on the bin lids, even the oldies that find it hard to jump, in hope that the sun shining on the bins will somehow warm their bodies. Quite clever, if you think about it, but I can't see it working too well. I hear them sneezing a bit too much for my liking, their noses running, their eyes weeping, and I pray.

"Please, God, don't let any die this winter, please. Don't let them be too cold."

And with every winter that arrives, my sister and I say to each other, "We need to help them. They're all going to die soon if we don't."

My feet hurt on the ice and snow as I trudge through to the feeding areas where I lay food under old, abandoned vehicles and inside large dog huts. Birds look down at me through the derelict roofless barn. I'm going back to the Palace Lounge, and I have to make sure all the cats are fed before my long shift. I'm not being bullied by Blackwell any longer. No way.

*

Rich is a big tipper. He arrives with a carrier bag containing car jump leads and a whip. What are the jump leads for? It turns out he wants me to tighten them around his balls, getting off over me wearing PVC and whipping him.

"I have a wife," he tells me. "But we don't fuck, or should I say she doesn't fuck me the way I need."

I can't lie, I quite enjoy prancing around, purposely wasting his booking time, feeling myself up, cracking my whip.

"Watch me touch my firm arse. Don't you dare move an inch." I notice him hardening, and then standing erect.

"Please let me touch it."

"Not yet, you dirty man."

"Oh, please, I'll pay you extra. How much extra do you want?" And so the tipping begins.

"Every time you touch yourself, I want an extra twenty pounds, you hear me, you dirty man?"

"Yes, Cat, yes. Not a problem." He hoists his back up off

the divan and sits in the corner playing with himself, getting it harder, wanting and needing to touch it.

"Right, stop! That's enough."

He quickly places both palms down at either side of his body. "No, please, I want to touch it some more."

"That will be another twenty." I lash the whip on the floor.

"Yes, Cat, yes, yes." He touches himself again. "You keep count." I most certainly will. I'm in my element again. I'm sure it'd be torture for him to leave this place without being able to play with himself whilst I turn him on.

"Enough."

But he keeps touching himself.

"I SAID ENOUGH!" I lash the whip on his stomach.

"Oh, dear, sorry." He places both palms down.

Kneeling down, I push my derrière further out, pasting my lips with my tongue. "Close your eyes while I take my panties off."

"Yes, Cat."

"If you dare to so much as peek at me when I'm removing my panties, I'll whip you. You understand, you dirty man?"

"Yes, no peeking. No peeking. I fully understand."

"If you peek, that's another twenty pounds. You hear?" Manipulating him to my advantage. I know he'll peek—it's inevitable. I place the whip down. "I'm taking my panties down now, sliding them over my bottom."

He looks. "You peeked. I saw you. Now you owe me sixty pounds on top of your service fee."

"I couldn't resist, Cat, I'm sorry. Please don't be mad at me." Why would I be mad? You've just earned me another twenty.

I sweep my hair off my shoulders, kicking my panties away

from my ankles, and then turn back round to face him. "You're such a dirty man. You couldn't resist, could you?" Unzipping my PVC dress down the front, and then cupping my hands around my breasts.

"Get over here. Now." He attaches the jump leads to either side of his balls. Ouch! They must be painful, clenching him like that, but he does have duct tape wrapped around the sharp edges, so I guess. . .

"Get on your knees and suck me." He's being the dominant one now.

I kneel down on the carpet. The music is soft and low. He lifts off the bed and takes hold of my head, then begins sinking his length down my throat as I count in my mind, holding my breath; one, two, three, four. How many times is he going to ram my throat like this? Five, six, seven, eight, nine, ten. My breathing becomes laboured. I'm panicking a bit as he carries on. Eleven, twelve, thirteen, fourteen, fifteen, sixteen. How much longer can I hold my breath? Seventeen, eighteen, nineteen, twenty. He pulls out and I gasp. What is he thinking? He could have choked me.

"Get on the bed. Get comfy," he demands. Things have really changed now. He's in charge of me.

'Okay." I get on the bed like he says.

He stands over my face, feet digging into the mattress, and lowers down, hovering over me, with the jump leads hanging down from his ball sack, resting on my neck. If he dares trying to strangle me with these leads, I'll punch him, hard.

"Open your mouth, you dirty girl. Get this in your mouth, you dirty bitch. Take it." He's getting carried away.

I inhale a mouth full of air and get ready for the worst. I

cannot put my trust in this man. Even a regular can come up with new tricks. He plunges into my throat again. One, two, three, four, five. Okay, let me see if he's going to repeat the ramming sequence. Six, seven, eight, nine, ten. I need to pull off, but I can't, as my head is jammed down on the mattress by the jump leads and his body strength is pounding on top of my face. Eleven, twelve, thirteen, fourteen, fifteen, sixteen. . . I have never, ever, ever been forced to hold my breath for this long. I try lifting him up. Damn it, he weighs a ton. Seventeen. Eighteen. I try pushing him away with my hands, but he surges harder. He's stronger than me. Nineteen, twenty. That. Is. It! I've had it. He stops at twenty. I gasp for air. What a complete jerk! I wonder what else he has up his sleeve. I bet he's never done this to his wife.

"Can I ejaculate twice?"

"There isn't a lot of time remaining." I can't be bothered putting in the effort. I mean, for heaven's sake, he hasn't even finished once yet. It's not shaping up to be the best first day back at the office, if I'm honest.

"Ah, all right, another time." I don't know if there will be a next time. How can I let him ram my throat like that again?

"Stand up." He slaps my backside. I swear I'll get him back right where it hurts if he carries on. Whack, I smack him back. "That'll be another twenty pounds for smacking my arse." Again, he slaps my backside. "Right. That. Is. Enough. Another twenty for that." I reach out and squeeze the clamps as hard as I can. "Take that, you bastard." Oh shit, what have I done?

"You fucking disobedient bitch, dirty bitch, dirty bitch." He lashes out and slaps my backside again. Now he owes me more.

"We only have a few minutes left." He needs to know I won't be going over the allotted time.

"Give me a kiss." Don't try and distract me. I know how long is left. 'Suck it once more, then I'll finish off."

Here goes. He lays flat on the bed with his head propped up by the pillows. "Go on, deep throat me. Show me how much of it you can take." His fingernails dig into my scalp.

"I will, but not too much because it hurts my throat."

"Just do it."

Yet again, he can't control himself. One, two, three, four, five, six, seven, eight, nine, ten. Just ten more rams and he can get out of my throat. Eleven, twelve, thirteen, fourteen, fifteen, sixteen, seventeen, eighteen, nineteen, twenty. I pull back off.

"Time's almost up." I wish he would hurry the fuck up.

"Get that condom."

I lay back, widening my legs. His eyes meet mine. I grab a rubber and he watches me put it on him. He climbs on top of me. The jump leads are digging on the insides of my legs—how annoying. It doesn't take him long to finish. All done.

I walk into the shower cubicle and pass my hand over the sensor switch. The water is warm but cools my flushed body.

"What have you been doing today?" I make casual conversation.

"Just done a little bit of painting this morning before I came to see you."

"What are you doing later tonight?"

"Nothing much. I've recorded a couple of TV programmes, so I'll probably watch them."

I step back into my PVC. He reaches inside his tweed

jacket hung on the back of the door and pulls a wad out. He pays me for the extras (he'd paid me upfront for the standard service before we canoodled). I open my boudoir door and step outside.

"Thank you. I will inform the receptionist you won't be long. You don't want my next booking walking in on you, do you?" I laugh pleasantly and kiss him farewell. Back downstairs, I place my wage in my locker. In that respect at least, it's good to be back.

A few days later, Rich returns.

"Will you fetch more outfits for me to see you wear?"

"I'll have a look what I've got." Checking my kinky outfits, dilly-dallying, will be knocked off his time. I make my way through the hallway, away from him. Rummaging through my case, I grab a handful of outfits. A red PVC skirt, some matching PVC knickers, patent black dress. He can select what he likes the look of.

"If you piss in my mouth, I'll pay you extra."

I play with him, thinking about his proposal. He watches me.

"Go on, then. Might as well. Lay down in the shower cubicle. That's where I'll do it."

"I'll play with my dick whilst you piss on me."

I hover over his face. He opens his mouth wide and begins to play with himself as I comply with his wishes.

As he re-dresses, I realise there's a market for this specific kind of domination of clientele. Servicing him makes me wonder whether to open a parlour that has specific rooms that cater for fetishes, dungeon-type rooms that will make my business stand out from the crowd.

"Rich, jot your number down on this piece of paper. If I ever leave here, we can keep in contact."

"Yes, indeed." He writes down his number. "All fine, but don't message or phone me at night as I have a wife."

CHAPTER SIXTEEN

William The Conqueror.

Most people don't make a final decision on what they'll name their pet until they've met it, and the same goes for a child before it's born. I didn't know a pet would find me either. But he did.

Will. William. His name comes to me because after everything he's been through—possible abandonment, being dumped, not knowing where his next meal would come from, if he'd even manage to forage—he is a warrior, a fighter, a leader, a conqueror.

He wasn't born at the homeless barn cats colony. Why do I think he was dumped? He is the most feral cat I've ever had the pleasure of meeting. He hisses like no other. He runs off like a shot, lashes out like a lion, shows his claws if I get too close; hardly any strays would act like this. He didn't just turn up. I believe someone knew we feed feral cats there, knew he'd have daily food, fresh water and a place to sleep outdoors. But did it ever cross their minds when they chucked him out of their vehicle that he may not be accepted by the colony, that he may run and keep running, or go in search of his original home and get lost? That is the risk those people took. Probably because they had no love for him. Luckily, I do. Maybe someone took one look at William and thought he would need to go to a farm, or he'd have to be euthanised. He can't be homed, he's too aggressive.

I phone Kitty. "Sis, a cat has turned up that I've never seen before."

"Could the cat be lost?"

"Not sure. I don't think so because he's hissing at me when I go near him." I have a gut feeling this cat is a he because he is well built, but you never know.

"If you can't get close enough to stroke him then what are you going to do?"

"I need to trap him, scan him, see if he has a microchip, see if he's lost."

Once trapped, I take him to the vet to be sedated- because believe me, he can't be handled by anyone. I find that he hasn't been microchipped, so I ask for that to be done when he or she is neutered. They confirmed the cat is a he, but says that he's already had the snip, proving he's been neutered by someone and not chipped, maybe a cat charity, making it even sadder that he could've been dumped on us. Cats that are neutered should really be microchipped by the vet at the same time, but this boy hadn't been, so there's no link back to whoever was originally responsible for him.

It's true that I'll never know where he was born or whatever happened to his siblings or his mother. Where they tuxedos like him? Did the person who abandoned him think he would be better living as a feral with a colony caretaker than being euthanised? If that was the case here, then I'm happy they chose me to be his new caretaker. Sadly, though, despite my very best efforts, it's becoming clear that the barn colony is no place for any cat.

The derelict barn's roof is caving in. There are holes everywhere and neither rainfall nor snow can be stopped from seeping in. And that darned side-lashing rain? Well, that drenches the poor barn kitties too, and when it's cold as well, the rain is lethal. Have you ever been freezing cold and wet in the rain?

*

London.

A woman with bobbed black hair and grey roots, wearing a stone-coloured tweed suit, is about to take the stand on the main stage in the Elizabethan Banqueting Hall. Members of the Middle Temple are seated upon blood-red leather and oak chairs in the vast hall, tables stretching from end to end, everyone in formal, professional attire.

The hall smells ancient and musty, as if it has been standing here for thousands of years. Apparently, sections of this building were damaged in the Great Fire of London, and then rebuilt. The walls are covered in small wooden plaques, names engraved on them in gold leaf, probably names of barristers and judges who once dined here, too. You could hear a pin drop in this hall.

To get us here I spent hundreds of pounds on train tickets and paid for a smart hotel for the night. I left my sister to do her thing.

"How did it go, Kitty?"

"The speaker took her time. She was powerful in her stance, banging her speech papers on the wooden lectern, bang, bang, bang. 'Welcome, fellow members'. She paused. 'What an elegant crowd you are. I'm particularly pleased to see so many women with short and tidy hair pulled back from their faces'."

"Carry on, Kitty," I encouraged.

"Well, I thought, that's her liking me out of the window then, as my hair isn't tied back off my face; it's long and flowing. What was she getting at? Having long hair doesn't mean I'm less capable of becoming a barrister or less intelligent than the next woman who has short hair. Does she believe all women should have shaved heads? It's as if she was telling the women there that they need to look like men to be taken seriously. What an insult. It seems some of the seniors of this profession are sexist and want to eradicate any feminist who might have dared to creep into their world."

"Bitch," I say.

Kitty has started the Master's degree and part of the course is to dine at her chosen Inn of Court, which is the Middle Temple. There are several parts to this event, with speakers during the day, some law-based activities in between, then more speakers, and then dining in the evening with other fellow members of the Middle Temple.

Brooding on the speaker's insult, Kitty tells me she didn't take in anything else that speaker said.

"The next speaker was an older male. He said if you know of anyone whose surname is Temple, or Templar, they most probably come from the line of Middle Temple judges and barristers, who had illegitimate children with prostitutes in

London some hundred years ago. Because the prostitutes had no way of keeping the babies safe while they plied their trade, they would dump them at the doors of the judges and barristers who got them pregnant. And so, the judges' wives would adopt their husbands' illegitimates."

"Wow."

"And if dealing with a full day of sexism isn't enough to put anyone off, make anyone give up on this career, the rest of the other speakers waffled on about how public funding of family and criminal cases has been cut, so their income is a lot less. How work is becoming tougher to attain because there's so much competition from new graduates, and the cost of living in England is becoming higher so it's not even worth trying to be a barrister! Seriously, one speaker even said that if anyone does become a barrister, they won't gain a reputation for at least fifteen to twenty-five years, so they'll only be able to enjoy the job's benefits in a quarter of a century's time, and that's if they're lucky. Blah, blah, fucking blah. Three hours of constant put-downs. Now I'm asking myself why the heck I've wasted three years of my life on a law degree?"

"Don't feel like that."

"The majority of students there are male. The majority of the seniors there are male, too. Men. Men. Men. Am I punching above my weight, thinking I can become a barrister when I'm 'just' a woman?"

"Don't be silly. I have every faith in you, sis. I've coped with plenty of put-downs in the past. I've had clients say things to me like, I bet you've slept with hundreds of men, all shapes and sizes. Or, I don't know how you do it. Some ask, don't you feel ashamed of yourself with all the men you bed? And once a bloke even said to me, if you had a daughter would you want her doing this job? I know I wouldn't want my daughter here. And then there are those who walk out after I've serviced them, saying they've forgotten their wallets, and don't return. So, yes, I've been made to feel low, but I've become tough-skinned."

"All the times I've stayed awake till the early hours of the morning completing essays and revising for exams. Was it all for nothing? Did I do it just to become part of a sexist legal clique?" says Kitty.

That evening my sister and I are invited to dine at the Middle Temple Hall on the banks of the River Thames. After the lavish meal, a grey-haired male judge approaches the table.

"Where did you gain your degree then, young sir? Are you looking for a placement in London?"

The young man glances at Kitty then speaks to the judge, "I'm here as a guest, I'm not actually studying law."

"I recently gained an honours," Kitty butts in. "Do you know of any upcoming placements?"

"Oh, have you tried the tea here? It's ghastly." The judge steps away.

He didn't even acknowledge that she had spoken. Did he think she was an airhead because she has make-up on and hasn't cut her hair short? It seems being a woman is a drawback in this career. She's being ignored because he only wants to employ men. Being female isn't a downside in a career as a hooker, though. That judge would be paying me generously in my workplace. I'll remember his face all right. If he ever thinks of booking in, I'll tie him up and take domination to a whole new level.

CHAPTER SEVENTEEN

Hello Cat,
Lovely to hear from you. Would be great to meet with you.
When you arrive, give me a call on the phone number on our
website and we will arrange a convenient time for an interview.
Best wishes,
Esmeralda
Platinum Heels

So, no guarantee I have an earner for a few weeks over there
whilst I'm seemingly on holiday, but still an opportunity for
an interview. Keeping on a positive note, then, working today
will help towards the flight costs for plane fares for Adonis and
I. He's fallen out with his girlfriend and could do with a break.

These cats are costing a fortune. I've started to open my
heart to these cats. They make me feel for them, big time. They
have me wrapped around their little paws and their fates lie in
my hands. How is it that such small, furry things can control
you, make you their servant? They just can, and they do.

*

When I was sixteen, my mum signed up to a phone-sex chat line as she wanted to work from home. Being a single mother of three back then, it was harder for her to get out of the house for work, and she had to put food on the table somehow. I used to toy with the idea of doing it myself to make money.

The phone would ring. "Hi, it's Raunchy Rebecca." I would overhear my mum.

Little did my mum know but when she was out of the house, I'd answer her calls. Back then I didn't really know how to talk sexy to any man, but it came naturally.

After I'd kept that first client on for two hours, I quite liked the naughty talk.

"Hi, I'm Sexy Samantha. How are you today?"

"I'm fine now I've heard your voice. What will you do to me, Sexy Samantha?"

"What do you like?"

"Everything."

"What would you want me to do?"

"I want you to take your panties down for me and let me inside."

"Do you now? What did you say your name is?"

"I really do. Jake."

"Jake, do you want me to tell you what I'm wearing?"

"Please."

The calls were mostly like this: me being a tease and just going along with the flow, trying to keep them on the call for as long as possible so they spent more to pay my mother's bills. And I wasn't always named Sexy Samantha. Before the calls took place, I was prompted by the telephonists who forwarded the call to me.

"Hi, love, today you're called Hot Hannah."

"Naughty Nina is your name for this call."

Tempting Tanya. Teasing Tina.

Sometimes my high school best friend would get involved, and she wasn't shy at all, so she didn't mind having a laugh joining in on the sexy talk. We could have got my mother sacked at times with the belly laughs that came out.

I would have the clients on the chat lines for hours sometimes. "Let's play I Spy," I would say to the callers. The company couldn't understand how my mother managed it. I was a hit.

*

Before going up to join a new client, I head to my locker to spray my perfume. The top notes are almost edible, wild strawberry and mandarin. The middle notes and base notes are aphrodisiacs, so I expect to make this guy pounce on me when I enter. A subtle smell sets the mood. I can close my eyes and be charmed by a man simply because he is wearing a pleasing aftershave.

"Hi... I haven't met you before, have I?" I dim the spotlights. He's a handsome stranger to me. I want to get to know him. He seems a tad nervous, fidgeting slightly.

"Wow, you are staggeringly gorgeous," he compliments me. "You're so pretty, it's making me nervous."

There's something edgy about getting it on with a stranger for the first time. I like the thought of it. He's appealing to the eye.

"You're quite a stud too." Where has this guy been all my

life? He is hot, dusky, dark-haired and has a wicked smile. A bit of playtime isn't wrong. Well, not in a massage parlour, anyway.

"You were recommended to me by a friend of mine."

"Recommended. Really? What friend would this be?"

"A girl who used to work here, she asked me whether I'd met you before and when I told her I hadn't she said I don't know what I'm missing. 'Cat is one of the finest in the business,' she said." He licks the edges of his lips. "And she isn't wrong, is she?"

"Which girl?"

"Sophie."

"Oh, Sophie. How nice of her." She didn't need to pass on custom. She just did so out of kindness. Thank you, Sophie. I flick back my silky hair, sensing he fancies me. But enough casual talk: down to business.

"So, what is it you like? May I ask?" Grinding against him, running my tongue over my top lip.

"You know, the usual, nothing too drastic."

We share a sensual kiss. I dip my hands down his firm body and he's hard. This will satisfy me. I cannot wait to get my lips around this.

He kneels down and I take him in my mouth whilst he's gripping my backside. Watching in the mirror beside me, I examine his impeccable reflection from another angle. I see he's studying my body closely. He licks his fingers and touches my sex in circular motions, as I carry on sucking him. He sure knows how to touch.

*

Mid shift, my mum is waiting to collect Petal after a

vaccination, but I get a phone call from the receptionist at the vets.

"Can we leave the cat till tomorrow now? The thing is, we've just been so busy."

"No. Sorry. You can't leave Petal in that carrier till tomorrow. She's been waiting for this appointment for weeks."

"Leave it with me. I'll speak to the vet."

What the hell? Why are my feral cats different to any other cat? I'd dropped Petal off in a special crush carrier so they could handle her inside the carrier. She should've been in and out.

Feral cats are often brushed off in society. Many vet practices don't really want to deal with feral cats, and some make up all sorts of excuses to not fit them in. I usually get given the very last appointment, although they urge me to bring the cats in for the very first appointment time. I don't really see that as humane when the feral cat can't even stand up, so they have no option but to do their business in the carrier. They can't even have a drink or food either. It's cruel, but I have to refrain from arguing the toss for the cats' sakes.

I force myself back into work mode: on to the next client. "Hey, honey, I say as I come into the room, we haven't seen each other for ages. Well, it feels like ages."

"Have you missed me?" He winks at me. Must I tell him the truth? No, I haven't missed him. And what is it with his constant winking?

"Yes, I've been thinking about you." I give a slight smile and flutter my eyelashes.

"Great to know, because I think about you every day, Cat."

"Every day?"

"Yes, every day, Cat." He winks about six times.

"Wonderful."

Ten minutes into the service and he's still got a fixated stare going on. What's with his creepiness? He tugs me towards him again, this time wrapping his arms across my back. I can't move. The tip of his pointed nose is pressing against mine. I can see his eyes at either side of his nose open wide as he forces his lizard tongue into my mouth again. I guide him to the bed.

"I think my panties need to be taken off."

In one swift movement he draws my knickers down my legs. This is the fastest motion I've ever witnessed, it's literally one second and my panties have disappeared to the bottom of the bed. If he's ripped them, he's paying for them. Within moments he's slurping, licking, sucking. Oh, my! What felt creepy before is perfect now and I can't control this euphoria. I can't deny that I want to be pleasured and he's giving me what I need, sorting my physical needs right out.

"Stand up, Cat. Let's do it against the mirror. I want to see your tits squashed up against the mirror."

Palms on the mirror. Legs apart. He comes up behind me and rubs up against me. I begin to feel him pushing it up my sex. I moan in genuine enjoyment.

"Squash your tits against the mirror more. Yes, those tits look immense. Now, lay your body on the edge of the bed. I want to do you off the bed."

And before I know it, he's done. As I'm washing in the shower cubicle he asks, "Would you ever consider doing an escort job outside of here, and go with me to meet another escort? I'd pay you well."

"Possibly."

He gets out his phone and shows me a picture of the escort. She's tanned, has silky, brunette, mid-length hair and a slim figure with long legs. I actually quite fancy the look of her.

"I don't see any harm in it. Have you met her before?"

"Yes, I've seen her plenty of times. I've shown her your picture on the website too and she's keen to meet you."

"But my face is blurred out on the website."

"Yes, but from your body she likes the look of you. I told her about you."

"I'll take your number then." If it pays more, it's worth it. Before I move on to the next client, I call the vet again.

"Hi, I'm ringing about Petal. Did you manage to vaccinate her? It should only take a minute to do, really." I'm livid. Poor Petal. Petty. Pet.

"Yes, we managed to squeeze her in."

Thank goodness. That's one good thing that happened today.

*

Every week Greaves books me for an hour. "It's cold in here now with the air conditioning on," Greaves complains. "Don't worry, it'll soon get hot again." I trail light kisses down his neck, avoiding his mouth area. "Let's sixty-nine." I'm going to try to finish him off quick as I want to finish on time today.

How much time have I wasted on this hand job? There are fifteen or so minutes left until the end of my shift. If the boss was here, I'd be afraid to tell her about this ordeal and the fact

I want to refuse Greaves. After all, this place is her business, her income. It's why she drives a Maserati convertible and how she owns five houses.

I can feel Greaves jerking in delight. "Oh, yes."

"Does my hand feel okay?"

"Yes, it feels more than okay," he mutters, "I don't know how much longer I can let you tug me for though. It's too sensitive."

"I'll do it slower."

"Stop! Stop! I can't take it anymore."

"Time's nearly up, Greaves."

"Okay, I'll finish off now." And so he does.

"Cat," he says as we dress. "I'm sure I saw you the other day. You were in a house. I could see you through the window, getting changed. It looked like you, anyway."

Is he a stalker? Why is he looking through people's windows whilst they're getting changed? Pervert. Does he know where I live? Has he put a tracker on my car? Does he want to kidnap me? My mind works overtime.

"Where?"

"Can't remember. Tell me where you live, and I'll tell you if it was you."

I'm not telling anyone where I live, but maybe he already knows my address. Maybe it was me he saw undressing.

"It probably wasn't me. . . Anyway, see you soon. I have to go now."

Is he going to follow me home when I leave?

The bulky security guard walks me to the car park at the rear of the building. This guard is one of the only men who doesn't stare at me in a sexual way. He never looks at my boobs when he's talking to me, never looks at my rear end as I walk away from him and always talks to my face. He's respectful.

I lock my car doors immediately; fearful I'm being followed. I drive away and I can hear bellowing from a main road bar. Drunken men yowl as I drive past.

"Wahey! Wahey!" Their jeering becomes louder.

A group of ten men are staring at me. They seem to be excited about the fact I've finished my shift, as though they've never seen a hooker before. Grow up: prostitution has been around for hundreds of years. Their mothers were probably on the game. Pulling away, I race through my gears, passing another bar where men are also crowding. Maybe Greaves is there. Maybe not. Maybe he's behind me in his car. Maybe not. I approach the traffic lights fast and decide to go for it on amber, inches off another car. I rush, overtaking other drivers, steering onto the motorway.

I keep glancing in my rear-view mirror. It's dark. I don't think anyone's chasing me. I'm not sure. I pull off the motorway. If Greaves knows where I live, he'll be waiting on my street.

Arriving in the shadowy street, outside my place, I reach inside the glove box for something sharp, anything. A plastic CD case? For goodness' sake, is that all I have to protect myself? If he attempts to capture me, he'll be in for a shock. I'll ram this CD case down his throat. This job has turned me into a fighter. I'm a tough bitch now.

Running as fast as a wild animal, forgetting my suitcase in the boot, I open my front door, flicking the lights on. I slam my front door behind me. Top bolt, bottom bolt, locks and chain. I rush to my living room, drawing my curtains, hiding. If he's awaiting a strip scene, he has another thing coming. I pour myself a stiff whisky. I sip and sip it again. My nerves are easing off. What the heck am I doing for a job?

I head into the bathroom, slamming my whisky down on the cabinet. I run a shower. I've lost count of how many showers I've had at work. The warm water hits my body. I'm on my own tonight. I light a candle in my lounge.

"If I won the lottery," Greaves once told me, "I would rescue you from this place." Apparently, he's created a website and hopes for it to pick up so he can 'save me'. I don't need a man to rescue me. And he'd be the last person I'd choose anyway; if anything, I need rescuing from men like him. Setting up my own business has never looked so appealing. Being the boss, not having to service clients, not having clients getting attached—emotionally attached, physically attached—attached in any way.

*

The next day, I'm due to visit the sexual health centre. You can't enter unless you are a sex worker. It's strictly for prostitutes here and the majority of them seem to be street workers. It is smack-bang in the middle of a renowned streetwalking area, so it wouldn't shock me if a punter were to pull up beside me right now and ask for business. I have dark sunglasses on, trying to hide my face as I walk over to the buzzer. I've brought Erin with me. Someone buzzes us in.

"Hi, sign in please and then take a seat in the waiting area until your names are called out," a grey-haired lady says. The nurses are casually dressed, walking around with clipboards. I remove my sunglasses.

"Do you want a cup of tea or coffee? Biscuits?" another lady offers.

"No, thank you," we both answer.

"They give you biscuits and brews here?" Erin whispers, amazed.

We're both handed a sheet of paper on a clipboard to fill out. I give false details. You can give real details of your name, date of birth, age, address and place of work, but I'd rather not. They know where I work, but that's all. I peer over at Erin's sheet. She has given her real name and home address, which I'm surprised about because she has a child. Wouldn't she rather protect them? If this place sense they have to intervene then they will involve the police without asking for permission. I'm sure they can clearly see that we're of the highest calibre, so I doubt the nurses here will phone the authorities on us. We don't take drugs. We don't cause trouble. We are harmless.

As we wait, there are several women seated in a corner having their nails manicured. Others are having their hair styled and make-up done in the other corner. Who would have thought a place like this existed? There's an open kitchenette to the right side, and friendly support workers hovering round, providing a shoulder to lean on. I guess everyone needs someone to talk to when times are hard. Many street workers have domestic violence in their lives, and addictions. They work to feed their habits. Most of them end up losing their children, which probably makes them go even more off the rails.

"You can get your nails done here for free if you want."

"No thanks," Erin turns her nose up at this. Some of the

street girls are quite loud and boisterous. "I can tell they're drunk and high on drugs. Let's stay away from them."

The other girls are glaring at us. I clutch tightly onto my handbag. Some of them look rough.

"Where do you work?" a street worker asks me.

"TPL."

"Parlour work isn't good nowadays."

I feel slightly sorry for her because she's dressed in a worn-out tracksuit and her hair is full of knots. She wouldn't get a job at The Palace Lounge.

"It's busier than the streets, love."

"I've tried a parlour once before, but it wasn't busy for me." As she talks, I can see she has brownish, stained teeth. Maybe that's from the drugs.

"Erin, please." The nurse waves her hand in the air.

Sitting patiently on the sofa I wait for the next slot after Erin. This drug addict hasn't got an appointment; she's here for support and for the activities. There are posters on the wall calling for information about a missing prostitute, a reminder of how dangerous it can be out on the streets. Erin makes her way back over to me after being seen.

"The nurse is waiting for you. She told me to tell you. It's great here."

"Won't be long, Erin. Did you get condoms off the nurse?"

"Yes, I've got about twenty off her."

"That isn't enough. I'll ask for more."

"I know, tell me about it." We both laugh at how many condoms we go through every day.

I make my way to the room where the nurse is waiting for me and close the door behind me.

"You're due your vaccination booster today, so I'll prepare it for you now." Gosh, it's not just the cats needing vaccinations now! "Do you need any condoms?"

"Please, as many as you can spare. I have to buy my supply from work at five pounds a pack, so I'd really appreciate it."

"I'll give you a couple of packs; they're all accounted for, believe it or not." She hands over some packets, barely a week's supply. Oh well, any is better than none, I suppose.

"Strip the bottom half of your clothes off, and then lie down on the bed and cover yourself with the paper towel."

"Alright."

"Let me know when you're ready. I'll close the curtains for you."

"I'm ready."

"Right. Put your legs at either side and shuffle your bum down the bed. This may feel a little cold, but it won't be inside you for long." She lubricates a clamp. "Just relax. . . I'm going to take some swabs from inside you."

It's all over in a moment.

"Do you still have the same number? I'll text you with the results next week."

"Yes, I'm still on the same number."

"Take care."

"Thank you. Have a nice day." I pick up my free condoms and exit. I want to be away from here as quickly as possible. I don't want anyone else I know—cat associates or anyone else—seeing me coming out of a prostitutes-only clinic.

CHAPTER EIGHTEEN

"Cat? Is it okay that someone has booked in with you for three consecutive bookings?" the receptionist asks.

"Sure." I always accept any bookings that come in, as nobody knows how the day's shift will pan out—whether there will be an influx of traffic through the doors or not.

"He's a regular. He's been coming here for years. He books in as Dixon."

He's ten minutes late, arriving at seven-forty instead of seven-thirty.

"I couldn't get away from work."

"It's coming off your time, sweetie. We close at nine, remember." The receptionist's tone is stern.

"Yeah, no worries, no worries, cool. Which bedroom is she in?"

From what I can see from peering into the lobby area, he looks tall. He dresses like a gangster or a rapper, wearing a thick gold chain around his neck, a baseball cap and excessively large gold sovereign rings over his fingers. Obviously likes to flaunt his money. His striking emerald eyes catch my attention; Egyptian-shaped and absolutely stunning.

"She's in bedroom five today. Go up, get a wash and she'll be with you shortly."

"He's a proper scally, him. All he wears is tracksuits," Sunshine blurts from behind me. She seems to enjoy telling me he's been with her before. She's coming across as jealous that he's booked in with me and not her this evening.

"Hi there," I approach him while he's still in the steaming shower. I'm wearing nothing but a baby-blue bikini set and patent white platforms.

"Hel-lo there." His enchanting emerald eyes look me up and down.

"I like the water hot, like my women," he laughs out loud at his own joke. "Can you fling me the towel, my jewel?" He's bewitching, I won't lie.

I casually pass him a dry towel as he steps out of the shower, his muscular body tempting me to touch it.

"Are you part Arabic in origin?"

"Most people think that because I'm light skinned, but I'm not. I'm a full breed. I've had a blessed life. Blessed in looks and money. Like you." He winks at me.

Not everyone is attracted to a gangster's ways, but the confidence shining from him appeals to me. All species of the animal kingdom seek confident mates to bear offspring with. He takes at least six minutes to dry, taking his time. Most clients can't dry themselves fast enough.

"I prefer a slow service, Cat. I want to take my time. That's why I booked over an hour with you."

"I'd like to know what you like then, so I know exactly what pleases you."

"Lie on your belly. I'll give you a massage."

I'm ecstatic. The tables have turned. Can it be true that he's paying to treat me to a massage? What a revelation. I strip off my bikini and turn onto my stomach. I hope this is going to be soft and relaxing, and not an aggressive sports massage. He smoothers body lotion over my legs, rubbing his soft palms in circular motions on my shoulders. His sublime touch is forcing me to sink lower onto the pillow.

I'm getting turned on as he slowly gives me an intimate shoulder and back massage, relieving my stress, relaxing my muscles. Where has this man come from?

"Tell me if anything I'm doing isn't all right. Okay, Cat? Trust me."

"I'm in heaven."

He transcribes perfect circles upon my back, starting small by kneading with his knuckles up my spine and then back down, repeating his movements. I wish I could get a massage like this every day. He runs the tips of his fingers gently down the sides of my spine in a neat line, and it's sensational. This guy knows exactly how to turn on my senses.

He traces up towards my backside and begins to delicately kiss my bare bottom, beginning to slightly lick my skin, licking inside each of the tops of my legs, towards my privates. I understand, from experiences with other clients, that he may now want to give me oral. As I move to roll over onto my back for him, he places his hand firmly on my shoulder bone.

"No. Stay down, I'm not done yet." His voice is calm yet forceful.

Strange. . . I assumed he wanted to lick between my thighs, but he doesn't. He begins to trail excessive licks all up my back. I presume at first that he'll only give me a few strokes of his tongue to turn me on, but I'm wrong. His spit begins to cover my entire back. He licks me with his full tongue, strong hard strokes, getting carried away. I look back at him and he's drooling like a dog. Well, I'm not on fucking heat, so he needs to calm down. But, no, he lashes the back of his tongue upon the bottom of my back. Doggy licks all the way up to my shoulders, about fifteen times. Fuck, I'm absolutely drenched in his spit. We're a good half-hour into his eighty-minute service, so there's another fifty minutes left of this. I turn my head back round and look away. I know if I stop him and walk out I won't receive my payment, so in the back of my mind I keep reminding myself he has given me an award-winning massage prior to this, and so I must grin and bear his licking ordeal. I turn round to look at him again and his eyes have become possessively evil. He's wheezing between every long, drawn-out lick.

Fifteen more minutes go by, I think, or maybe twenty, and his saliva covers my spine and shoulders. Hang on a minute, stop right there. He begins to lick my neck and ears, and then both sides of my cheeks, panting deeply. I try to lift my head up, away from him, but he pushes me back down into the mattress. I feel I'm being forced to allow this, and now I'm getting anxious. I can feel my heart palpitating. I feel trapped. What the heck is he doing now? He attempts to lick my arms thoroughly, up and down, going at it like he's trying to draw blood, and then crazily licking each of my fingers, one by one.

I can now smell his spit drying over my body. I want to heave as I breathe in his drool. Please, someone stop him.

"Okay, err, are you finished?" He ignores me and keeps licking, on and on. Another ten or so more minutes pass. I'm getting more and more distressed. "Do you want me to play with you?" I blurt.

"No. I'm. Not. Done. Yet."

How can he not be done? He has licked my whole body, including my fingers and toes, and he says he's still not done. Does he want to lick my stomach or something? It's the only part of me he hasn't drenched in spit, apart from my tits. He can sling it.

"Oh, that tickles." He pulls my stomach towards his tongue. "Darling!" I yelp out, trying to grab his attention.

"Yes?" he speaks with his tongue dangling, as though ready to take another lick.

"You only have about ten more minutes left. Do you want sex?"

"Err... Yes." He has finally succumbed. "Did you like that?"

"Yes, I loved it. Now I'm ready for you." I lift my naked body up off my divan towards him and grab his hardness lightly. He's been hard this whole time. "Should I wank it?"

"No. I'm too turned on. Put one of them on." He nods towards the two condoms, so I grab one and open it. As I'm seated upon the bed, I get a waft of his saliva odour coming off me again. Can't this guy smell his spit on me?

He's now on top, in full control, pushing himself inside me slowly in missionary position. He caresses my hair with his palm, stroking it downwards. He is well endowed, and he feels immense.

"You're a fucking beauty, Cat." Five slow pushes inside me and he explodes inside the condom. I'm now aware of the rationale behind his ongoing licking. He wanted to drag our service out because he's a quick ejaculator.

"That felt amazing." I kiss him in delight. No more licking from him. I can shower, dress and go home.

He grins. "Really, was it amazing?"

"I've never had such an amazing build up before, in all my life." I hop into the shower cubicle.

"So, you'll be going home now?"

"Yes, darling." No more talking is needed from me, as I dry myself.

"You know you're the type of girl a guy like me would marry. Do you need a lift home?"

"No, I'm okay, thank you." I grab hold of my lingerie. "Thanks for offering though, darling."

I'd never accept a lift home off a client anyway. I don't want any client knowing what town I live in, let alone what street I live on, or the number nailed to the front of my door. I'll not gamble with my life. At least when we meet clients in work, they can't harm us or hold us hostage. When I work, there are always security guards on the door.

"There's your money." He spreads out the dosh.

"Oh, thank you, darling." I put the cash in my purse and dress myself speedily. I can be nippy when it comes to dressing to go home.

I still feel in distress from his licking. It's unusual, but I'm bothered in a way that I've never been before. But who can I tell? I can't tell the receptionist I've been licked for seventy minutes, and it has got to me. I can't tell the boss because she might think I'm not cut out for the job, and I can't tell my work colleagues as they may just think of it as a harmless lick. But to me it was more than just a lick. I felt as though my body was his to do whatever he pleased with. I felt I couldn't stop him as he kept telling me he wasn't finished with me and pushing me back down. I feel used.

Thankfully, I'm cheered up by a kind message from a cat friend:

Thank you for doing the hard part of actually rescuing and caring for these cats! Donating is easy and the least I can do to support your efforts.

Another kind message:

Hi, I'm glad you received the food and I'm glad it will be of help to you and the cats. Yeah, a shout out is fine, I will try to send more food next month when I've been paid again, shame it all revolves around money. You're doing an amazing job and we think you're a star. Take care.

Feeding the feral colonies does revolve around money, she's not wrong there. It's heart-warming to know that some kind people support the help I give these innocent animals, and nice to know not all people who know what I do think I'm a crazy cat lady. (By that I mean they know what I do for the cats; not what I do to please men. Nobody knows that, yet.) These lovely messages uplift me after what I've been going through lately.

*

"Oh, I don't know. I don't know. I don't know." Cassie walks into the changing room, laughing her head off.

"What don't you know, Cassie?"

"I don't know. I don't know. I don't know."

I leave her to it. I do wonder sometimes whether she knows what day it is, or even that she's working in a massage parlour.

"Some cunt shoved a fucking chewing gum up my fucking fanny," Cassie chuckles.

"What?" I place my hand on her fake-tanned arm, in shock. "Cassie, what happened?"

"The guy who I saw just then was licking me out and he found a piece of chewing gum stuck up there." She seems absent, her eyes in a distant dreamland. "Oh, I don't know. I don't know."

"That's disgusting, Cassie. Who did it?" I begin to giggle with her. Her laughter is infectious. "Who was it, Cassie?"

She places her wage into her work locker. "I don't know. It could've been up there for weeks." She holds the chunk of gum in her fake tanned hand, showing it to me. 'Look. The dirty bastard." She bins the gum.

Cassie doesn't have many regulars, only walk-ins.

A man in his mid-twenties strolls in. "Who's available?"

"At the moment we have Rainbow, Cat, Mercedes, Violet, Cassie, Sicilia and Leah." All seven of us. He can choose his pick of the crop.

"Can I not see any of the girls in person?"

I and three other girls come out from the changing room to introduce ourselves.

"Hmmm, who is the best? Who should I choose?" he smirks and mocks us to our faces.

"Go on then girls, give me a twirl." Rotating his index finger round in circular motions. "What are you waiting for then? Twirl around."

We all freeze. I've never heard any client speak in this demoralising way in the reception area before, belittling us, demanding we put on a catwalk show for him. He hasn't put forward any money, so I won't be spinning around for him. I'm not begging for his custom. We all remain silent, feeling humiliated.

"Excuse me. I don't think so," the receptionist interrupts. "You've just seen the girls in person, as you asked. They've introduced themselves to you and you can blatantly see how gorgeous they all are. So no, they won't 'give you a twirl'. Choose one or leave."

A huge feeling of relief settles over me, and I no longer feel worthless.

"Sorry. I'll book in with Cat then, please." There's a higher level of respect in his voice now, his tail in between his legs.

"Okay, what's your name?"

"Jazz."

What a shit session this is going to turn out to be, I think, as I meander towards room four. As I open the door to face him, he's drying off. "Sorry about that, before. My name is actually Adrian."

"No problem."

"I'm actually quite shy around girls."

We begin in doggy position and end in doggy. Only one position for him then, sharing an easy thirty minutes. He showers, chats some about his life, complimenting me here and there, and then gives me a lavish tip. As sweet as pie.

"You should give me your number in case I leave here, then I'll message you so you can still book in with me."

One week later, Jazz comes back (I know he said he's called Adrian in real life, but I call him Jazz). Good. I've got to keep the clients coming in so I can carry on doing cat work. The colony cats are due for another deworming, and they're in need of some self-heating blankets to help keep their little selves warm. On top of all that, I'm still saving up for the Master's my sister is doing, even though I'm unsure as to whether she's going to carry on studying. She's got one foot through the door, now, so it's a big decision to give it up.

"I've booked you for an hour," Jazz tells me. "And then for another hour after you've seen someone else."

He dims the bedchamber spotlights so low I can hardly see his facial expressions, but he's there, standing with no clothes on, dripping wet from the shower. Oops—he must be waiting for the towel.

"Here you go, here's a towel," I shout, as the music on the stereo is blasting loud too, playing chart music. Maybe he's extra nervous to see me.

"I've been thinking about you so much since the last time I saw you."

"How nice." I rest the other towel on the divan. He flings it on the floor, not bothering to dry himself properly. How strange.

He strokes my hips, and droplets of water trickle down to my ankles from his hands as we snog. He lightly turns me, so my back is towards the divan and pushes my body onto it, sliding my golden bikini briefs to one side. His wet tongue begins to lick my sex and I enjoy watching him and knowing he's paying me for this.

"Mm, you didn't do this last time."

"That's why I booked longer with you this time. I wanted to get to know you better, please you too, you get me?"

"Mm, I get you." I'm enjoying his licking.

He doesn't make me orgasm. Not everyone can, but I'd like to return the favour. I manoeuvre myself into a sixty-nine position, sucking him pleasantly, slowly, so his enjoyment lasts.

"I'm glad I met you, Cat," he says, as I gently suck him.

I can't reply as I have a mouthful. I begin to deep-throat him, picking up the pace. I wonder if he can handle my mouth. I rub his waist, which I hope he understands means I'm glad he met me too, or glad I met him, whichever way he wants to look at it.

"Fucking cool, that was. Best blowie ever. I'll be back in half an hour."

"Perfect, honey." I slap his behind, being cheeky, brightening the bedroom spotlights as he leaves, after he put the wad in my hand.

"Do you want any food bringing back in, sweet?"

"Oh, yes, honey, if you don't mind. I'm so hungry."

"What would you like? I'm going to a takeaway."

"Can I please have a sandwich? And can I have fries as well? I'll give you the money."

"Don't be daft, you don't have to give me the money for it." A true gent. I like that in a guy.

On his return, with my warm food, for his second hour's stint, I ask him, "Is Adrian your real name then?"

"In actual fact, my true name is Isaac." We seem to be best pals, eating our takeaway together on the divan.

"You need a table and chairs in here, Cat, so we can eat on it."

"Not everyone brings food in here."

"Next time I'll bring some candles in with me. Candlelit dinner."

"You're funny."

He's bought himself two sandwiches and two lots of fries, with four sides of fried onion rings. He has a big appetite. I notice he's got three mobile phones at the side of him.

"Why have you got so many mobiles?"

"I'll let you in on a little secret, Cat. I employ many members of staff in my enterprise. An enterprise that isn't legit but makes me a fortune."

"Businessman, are you?" I get the impression he's a drug dealer, so I change the subject and ask him about his family, his background, where he goes on holiday. Throughout his whole two-hour service all of his three phones are ringing and receiving text messages. Ring, ring, ring. Bleep. Bleep. Bleep.

"Hang on a minute, Cat, let me just get this call." He eventually moves away from the blow job I'm giving. I wait, kneeling beside him whilst he talks. "Mate, let me call you back, I'm just with a bird. . . Alright, safe."

Bleep. Another text. "One second, Cat, let me just reply to this text."

So, I go down on him again whilst he's busy. He's texting away, speedily. Ring, ring, ring. His other mobile phone. "I'll just get this other call." Stopping me again, answering another phone call. He pants deeply to the person who's calling. "Yeah [pant] go to that address I just sent you [pant] they wanted a ten bag but now they want a twenty-bag dropping off [pant]. Alright, safe."

Maybe he gets turned on at the thought of his employees

speaking to him on the other end of the phone line whilst he's in receipt of a blow job.

His body jerks. "Yippee," he says, as he finishes. "You're the best at sucking, you know."

"I should hope so."

"You are. Why do you think I came back, eh? Here, Sweet, there's your cash. Some extra for you, treat yourself."

I count the notes as he passes me my wage and there sure is a tip. He jumps in the shower cubicle. He dishes out cash as though he's got money to waste. Wish I had money to waste. Bet he doesn't have fifty or so cats to feed daily.

CHAPTER NINETEEN

"Where are you going looking all dressed up with make-up on?" A girl walks past who I've known for years. She spots me feeding the cats before my shift. It's none of her business where I'm going or why I've decided to put make-up on today. All I want to do is feed the colony cats before my shift.

"You've built a rod for your own back feeding all these cats."

"If I don't, they'll die."

"You need another hobby."

Oh really? Like she has a hobby.

"You need a baby."

I've come to realise that people have so many opinions about cats. . . and about babies. But she needs to keep her shitty opinions to herself before I tell her straight. You need to stop opening your legs to as many men as you can for free, not knowing who your baby daddy is.

For some reason, I guess because it's funny, but it just kind of makes sense that escorts often say, "At least I get paid for it and don't go around giving it away for free." And it can sound like the most ridiculous thing to say but if you think about it, we're just like any other girl in the 'real world'; it's merely a job. I've seen sex workers being hard to get with men in the 'real world' far more often than my other friends who aren't escorts.

*

Back in the Parlour, I find that both of them are dressed in nothing but black. Assuming this episode will be a threesome, I introduce myself to them. I've seen the man before.

The lady shows her teeth. "Pay my fee for booking in with her. I want her alone."

Now I'm thrown—she wants me alone?

"Of course, Lilith," he agrees.

She books me all to herself for thirty minutes. These people aren't any average couple, they're devil worshippers. They are known around these parts for wanting to be vampires, drinking red wine and calling it blood. Is she here to find out why he sees me? Does she want to know what I've got that she hasn't got? Why he pays me?

Vampire Husband wears a black studded leather jacket, black leather trousers and black spiky boots. All in black, always black. Oh, and also, a black leather t-shirt and matching black leather underwear. He has a thick grey streak running through his long black hair, poker straight, like a woman's. Today he looks as though he's patted talcum powder on his face to enhance the ghostly effect.

Vampire Wife has long, black, straightened hair too. She is wearing a black, tight-fitting PVC dress, with her oversized cleavage popping, and is covered in colourful tattoos. Her leather jacket is longer, helping to hide her pale skin on this cold spring morning. I don't even have to mention the colour of her nail varnish. Black is my favourite colour too, but not to this extent. It seems every day is Halloween for them.

Vampire Wife is now waiting in my boudoir. There are a few girls hiding in the changing room, probably hoping Vampire Wife won't select them. Apparently, she's been in before, looking at my picture on the wall, asking the receptionist which days I work. Angel had told me once me she'd seen a 'witchy looking woman' asking about seeing me. It arouses me watching porn scenes of girls giving oral to each other, so let's see how this pans out. Vampire Husband is sitting in the reception area listening to the giggles and whispers going on around him.

I open the boudoir door, kissing her sweetly and somewhat timidly. "What is it you want out of these thirty minutes?"

"Just to have fun." She's still dressed.

"Did you have a shower before you came?"

"Mm."

I kiss her again. My heart speeds up as I slightly rub her arm. What the heck should I do? I unclip my lingerie and kick my heels to the side, behind the closed door, then give her my bare boob, touching it to her lips. She looks into my eyes as she licks and sucks.

"Come here." I kneel on the bed behind her, taking her hand and leading her down beside me. I want to be in control here. I don't know what she may do to me if she's in control, and I remember her husband liked to bite me quite hard the last time I saw him. He'd told me to bite him even harder, and that his wife bites him till he bleeds in their bedroom. Crazy lady.

Rotating my naked body around, lowering my mouth over her privates, experimenting in a sixty-nine position, and then diving in for the kill, licking her with the tip of my tongue. She feels velvety on my tongue. She looks sexually attractive naked, with her curves, and covered in colourful tattoos. I begin to stroke her large breasts from on top, and then lick her some more, spitting on her, making her wetter. I slide two fingers inside her, pushing them deeper as I carry on licking her up and down.

"Yes, keep doing that with your fingers." Now her breath is warming up my sex. She carries on licking me from below. She's making me wet.

I grab hold of a vibrator and begin to slide it in and out of her, whilst licking her. She says, "Yes, yes, don't stop, don't stop," and then moans loudly in ecstasy. "That was amazing, that orgasm. I'm so glad I've seen you today, Cat." I pull my body from on top of her. "I've been trying to book in with you for weeks, but you're always fully booked."

I kiss her lips softly. "You can phone up the day before and reserve me in advance."

I might have enjoyed this session more if her partner was in the boudoir because we could've both played with him too, but she might have been jealous if I was licking her partner's balls.

"Are you not jealous that your boyfriend comes here?" I ask.

"Husband!" she corrects me angrily.

Who wants a snappy regular? Not me. I don't want her number.

Once I get my fee off her, she goes, and I take my time, smoothing out the bed sheets, positioning the pillows neatly in the centre of the bed and straightening out the towels, so I don't have to accompany her to the lobby. By the time I come out, they've gone. Why are all my colleagues looking at me?

"Go on, Cat, tell us what happened."

I don't know where to start.

"Tell us."

"Did you give her an orgasm?"

"Apparently so. Stop talking about it now."

"Do you think she'll come back again?"

"Don't know. It's up to her what she does. Anyway, I'm famished. When's lunch coming?"

*

"Let me look after you," my next client, Big, says.

Seriously, why do so many clients want to rescue me: Dolce Boy, Greaves, and all the rest?

"I'll take you abroad." Big travels the world; Dubai, Thailand, the far reaches of China, the Caribbean, all to set up deals for knock-off goods to sell in England. I suppose it's kind-hearted of him, offering to care for me.

"Please let me take you out for a nice meal." He sways from side to side, his eyes bloodshot.

"I'll think about it." Kissing him, tasting alcohol on his lips.

I'm talented at GFE, a professional. I'd most definitely be nominated for an Oscar for best actress of the year if the parlour was a movie studio.

As our kisses collide, I taste alcohol again, but this time it seems stronger, so he must have definitely had one too many drinks this morning, maybe in an attempt to calm his nerves. Hang on a minute. My lips are now tingling.

"Have you been drinking?"

"Just a little." A little? My tongue and lips are both turning

numb. Deeper tongue kissing. What's that taste? It tastes acidic.
My tongue and lips are now burning—something isn't right.

"Have you taken drugs?"

"How do you know?" He nods. "Before I came in, I had
cocaine. Pure cocaine." Showing off about the fact he's had
pure. Pfft. He's boasted about taking drugs on nights out with
his friends before, so it's obviously no biggie to him.

"My lips are numb. I don't want drugs in my mouth."

"I only had a little bit."

He touches my sex to arouse me, but his touch begins to
sting. For crying out loud, is there anywhere on this bloke's
body that isn't covered in cocaine? He must have it on his
fingers.

"Look, honey, you're not going to finish off. You've been
drinking and you've had drugs. Time's almost up and I need
to hop in the shower."

"Yeah, you're right. I gave myself a hand job before I came
here anyways." Make my job harder than it is, why doesn't he?

I'm ready to shower and leave the boudoir, but my legs and
hands feel shaky, my lips still numb. He's spiked me. Fucking
great. How am I supposed to see David, Ronnie, Giles and all
the others in this state?

"You've put a bit of weight on since our last meet, Cat."
Charming. He spikes me, then he insults me. I look in the
mirror at myself. Have I put on weight?

"I've signed up at the gym. It's all those snacks I've been
eating," I agree with him, as it's easier to agree in work than
to fight back.

"Let me take you out for a meal."

"No, then I'll get even fatter."

"This is my number. So many girls would be honoured to have it. Phone me when you get home, after work." He passes me his business card.

"Money please, babe. I'm running late and don't want to be shouted at by the receptionist."

I rush to the receptionist. "I need to speak to you."

"Come in here." She walks me into an empty boudoir, closing the door behind us. "What's up?"

"I've been spiked."

"What do you mean? Spiked?" Drugs are a no-no on these premises.

"I can't feel my lips or mouth, they're numb. I'm shaking. I need to sit down. Need a drink."

"Is he in your room? The one who spiked you?"

"Yes, but he didn't have the drugs on the premises. He took cocaine before he entered the room and passed it on through oral and kissing. I needed to tell you because I feel jittery. I don't know if I can see the next person yet, think I need to sit down."

"What a knobhead. He is a regular though. He hasn't done it to any of the other girls. Do you want me to have a word with him? I can get him banned from the premises if you think he'll do it again."

"It's okay, don't say anything to him. I'll see if he does it again next time." I can't ban too many people, or I won't have any returning clientele.

"I don't want you passing out on other clients."

"I don't think I'm going to faint. My hands and legs are trembling though."

"That could be the drug settling in. See how you go, have

a rest, and in the next ten minutes, if you think you're okay to carry on, I'll put your next client in your room."

I go in the ladies' changing room. "My last client just spiked me," I tell Angel.

"The loser." She's topping up her make-up, ready for her next client.

"He told me I'm fat. I'm not fat. I'm a size ten."

"How do you think I feel when guys say, 'Grab your tiny tits for me'?" She laughs. "I feel like telling them to grab their tiny you-know-what for me."

CHAPTER TWENTY

"It was planned. I was eighteen. He was my boyfriend, someone who I trusted my body with. He was a virgin too."

"Well, you've caught up now, haven't you? Even though you lost your virginity late, you must have slept with hundreds of men by now." He is laughing sarcastically.

I don't care about him inferring that I'm a slut. It's men like him who are stupid enough to fund the lives of girls like me. He has a strawberry blonde beard, but mousy blonde hair on his head, pushed over to the left side of his face. He was a virgin on first entering here, so he says, and left a non-virgin, obviously. But he didn't lose his virginity to me. Thankfully.

"Do you live with your parents?" he asks.

"No. Do you live with yours?"

"Yeah. I'm their only son."

"Do you have any sisters?"

"No, there's just me."

"Oh, right." I can't imagine what that must be like. I adore my brothers, and Kitty and I are best friends. And mum she's my world.

"Is it okay if we don't have sex? I just want to get to know you first."

"That's fine."

"I struggle to keep an erection."

"Do you want to take your clothes off anyway?"

"No." He doesn't undress, so I can't see the size of his privates. I'm curious. "Here's your money. My mum and dad have paid for you today."

Nobody has ever said that to me before. Sounds like he might be spoilt, as well as an only child. We talk, and I don't undress either. Easy. He goes on his way. I'm not sure if I'll see him again, but the following week he's back. This time it seems he wants some action, and I oblige. But there's a problem.

"I'm paying for you, so just wait one moment." He speaks as if he owns my body, without thinking of my feelings.

"Okay. Okay." I'm thinking, 'just hurry up and pay me then.'

"Ah. No. No. No. Look what you've done! I told you to stop touching it, and now you've got me stressed out and it's gone soft. It is all your fault, Cat." More spoilt brat behaviour.

"Calm down."

"Stop! Stop!" He shouts at me, which is why I name him Stopcock Shane. "Why is it small?"

"It's fine, don't worry." I comfort him, as he's embarrassed. The truth is, I only put up with his comments when he says crap like 'it is all your fault' because he's easy, and easy customers are always welcome. Stopcock Shane is a spoilt brat, no denying, but he has never sworn at me, bitten me, twisted my nipples or slapped me, so I'll just continue being passive.

On his third visit he's shouting again.

"No, it's too tight! You're going to snap me. Get off me. No! You're going to snap me."

"I'm not going to snap you. I'm strong, but not that strong."

"Oh, no! I've gone soft again." He throws himself down on the divan next to me in a childish tantrum.

He hasn't gone the whole hog with me yet. He's had a hand job here and there, that's it. He's frightened at the thought of me sitting on him.

"Should I play with you then, babe?"

"Yes! But don't patronise me by calling me babe."

"You make me laugh. You're funny, you. You're so funny. You need to book an hour with me next time, you do."

"I've got something to show you, Cat." He stands up off the bed, reaching into his coat pocket.

"What have you got there?" he holds a piece of paper tightly to his pigeon chest.

"It's a review of you, off the internet. I printed it off at home and last night I tossed myself off reading it."

"Did you? That turns me on. So, you wank off reading about me being fucked by another man?"

"I imagined we were fucking. Can we act this review out? Maybe it'll make me go hard again."

"Yes. Let's act it out. Let me read it." I take the review off him. "Oh, yes, I know who wrote this about me." I read it fully. "So. . . he had me in doggy position, it says, then I finished him off with a hand job on my boobs."

"Yeah, that's right."

"Let me bend over for you then."

"Yes, that might work."

"Put yourself inside me, Shane." I bend over so he can see my sex.

"I know it isn't very big. I bet you laugh at the size of me. I bet you see lots of guys who have big knobs, don't you?" In a puff of smoke, he goes soft again. I suppose with him it's purely a mind-over-matter issue. "Fuck! Why me? Why does this keep happening to me? Fuck my life."

"Don't stress, babe." I try to reassure him, forgetting he doesn't want me calling him babe. "It's fine. I'll make you hard again." I have to try, even though I know making him hard a second, third, fourth, fifth, sixth, seventh and eighth time in a sixty-minute period is tricky.

"I hate my life." His whole body seems to shrink beneath him.

Speaking of shrinks, he told me last time that he visits one on a weekly basis, a female psychiatrist. She gave him a colourful friendship bracelet, as a way of keeping his custom maybe. My type of friendship doesn't need a bracelet to get him to return.

"I've tried ending my life before."

"Many people in this world fight to stay alive with life-threatening illnesses or injuries. Life is precious, Shane."

"Yes, I know."

"I'm here for you as a friend. Always remember that. Here, write down your mobile number." I pass him a piece of paper and pen. 'If I ever leave here, I'll message you so you can book in with me."

"Like as an escort? Thanks, Cat." He writes down his number and passes me the paper. "I'm glad I met you."

He leaves with a big smile on his face. No doubt he'll return next week.

He does, lying on the bed, still clothed. "I never told you about Tammy, did I?"

"Tammy?"

"I met her here. She told me she loved me. She arranged to meet with me outside of this place, but then let me down and left me hanging around, waiting."

"That's bad, leaving you waiting."

"When I came in the following week she saw me, but then halfway through the booking she broke down crying, saying her boyfriend had beaten her up the night before. She said I was being too needy for her to cope with and had me kicked out for being aggressive towards her, apparently. But I wasn't."

He's telling me she broke his heart and lied to him, but Tammy and I both know she was purely doing her job, touching him intimately, pleasing him sexually, telling him words he wanted to hear to ensure that he came back for more. Some guys, especially those who struggle with insecurities, can easily become attached to a person who is overly nice to them, who is also giving them sex.

On his fifth visit, Tammy sees him hurrying off towards my boudoir. "I didn't like him anyway," she whispers. "Is he not too much for you in the room? Do you know what I mean? Too clingy? He is with me." She huffs and crosses her arms.

"Too much? No, not really. I let him know where he stands and don't lead him on. He's only a young man. Young men can become attached quickly if they're misled."

She looks at me with piercing eyes. I'm letting her know

that I'm aware she misled the virgin boy with the false hope of a relationship.

"I only got him kicked out because I'd been beaten up that weekend by my ex. I was really emotional."

"Oh, right." I face the mirror, topping up my lipstick.

"I was covered in bruises and Shane hugged me too tightly, and I'd told him to be careful with me. He was too clingy, demanding to see me outside of work, and so I burst out crying. He upset me."

I realise there are two sides to this story, her story and his. He had hurt her bruises and she was in an emotional state, regardless of him being clingy. I finish my make-up and go up to the boudoir.

"I saw Tammy on my way in," he says. "I hate her. She led me on and lied about having a boyfriend and children, telling me she dreams of me when she was supposedly in her bed alone. Liar!"

"Hmm. . . I see." I don't name-call Tammy in front of him. If she's over-friendly with her clients, then that must be the way she gets return custom: each to their own. She needs the money as much as I do. She's got kids to feed. I have cats to feed. But I don't want to hypnotise all of my clients into returning with false hopes that one day I may be their girlfriend. That is wrong. Nobody deserves to be led astray. I'll have fun with them and offer them exactly what they require sexually for a fee, but that's it.

Shane leaves after another hand job.

"What did you do in your job interview, Cat?" my next client asks.

"What do you mean?"

"How did they know you were good at your job? Did you have to sleep with the boss to be accepted?"

"No. I didn't have to sleep with the boss."

"Did the owner watch you sleep with someone else then, to see how ace you are in bed? Or did they give you a job because you're good looking?"

"No, definitely not, it's not like that here."

"It's like a dream, this place. I wish I could wake up here every morning."

Every morning? His wallet probably couldn't afford to wake up here every morning, plus I doubt he'd have the energy to have me every morning. I spruce up his life with a blow job whilst he's sat on the edge of the divan, and then I send him on his way.

Back in the changing room, I hear the receptionist call.

"Cat, is your room clean for when the next one arrives?"

"Yes."

"Have I got anyone now?" I ask her.

"We're waiting for Peter to appear, Cat. He should be here within the next five minutes. If he doesn't turn up, then I'll give you away to this next guy who is sat down over there." Give me away—as if I was at the altar.

"Thanks, honey."

After a few minutes: "Cat, I've sent Peter up to your room."

"Great. Thanks."

I've seen Peter umpteen times. He's an artist. Lovely fella. Likes a smooth back massage, gives me oral, then I toss him off whilst talking dirty.

*

Sometimes artists draw or paint cat portraits to help us set up competitions on the cats' social media to raise money to feed the colonies, and kind ladies take the time to knit blankets for the homeless cats' outdoor huts. Initially, we upcycled polystyrene boxes as cat huts, made a hole in the side of them and added straw and fleece blankets. They worked well in the summer months, keeping the cats warm and sheltered, but in the rain they leaked, so we bought some wooden huts that we had to build ourselves. Obviously, having never used a drill before, I asked my fella for help, and he built up ten of them for the barn cats colony. The garage cats tend to use the garage as a shelter, but the barn cats sadly don't have that option.

I make up alcohol hampers, perfume hampers, scented wax melt hampers and cat goodies hampers, all to bring in funds. One gentleman donated an alcoholic beverage hamper he'd won from another rescue organisation, so I could raffle it off again to buy cat food. There are some kind people out there. These people understand my dream: to take the feral, stray, injured, sick, unwanted and unloved cats away from their world of suffering and care for them in a sheltered, heated cat sanctuary. There they can live in safety, indoors and outdoors, on a big plot of land with cat safety fencing. Happy, with food, warmth, cleanliness, medication and love. Feral cats and strays need to have some outdoor life for their sanity. I want to provide a safe haven for them to either live out their days, or possibly be re-homed. Unfortunately, feral cats are very nervous around humans, but since I've been feeding them, some have become friendly. How great it would be to re-home the eligible, once-feral cats alongside the other stray cats in need. That would be purr-fect. I haven't made any concrete plans as yet, and I don't have a timescale for my dream, but ideally, I'd love for the feral cats' sanctuary to be situated in a rural area off the beaten track, with safety-proof fencing. I'd run it full-time, but would love to eventually have staff, or volunteers, aiding in cleaning, caring and feeding the feral and stray cats that need a safe haven. This place for them would have outdoor pens, big on space so the cats can still have vast areas to roam freely, but with a warmer indoor sleeping zone they can come in and out of as they please when the weather outside is unkind. It would look like heaven to a feral cat, with plenty of food to eat, climbing areas for them, cat trees, toys, lots of feral friends to socialise with, some catnip here and there. This is my dream of a place. But I don't want it to be just a dream, and I know that most dreams—not all but most—you have to work hard for.

In this day and age, no animal should have to suffer. There needs to be more shelters for unfortunate street cats, and this is something so close to my heart and—I am sure—many other people's hearts too.

*

I decide not to mention to Mr Gold what I'm back doing for a living, because tonight is about one another. No interferences. No drama. He's spared no expense bringing me here. The restaurant is perfect, and he is at his charming best.

My second cocktail arrives. It's called a Dalton's Atomic Experiment and contains a Jose Cuervo brand one hundred per cent blue agave tequila and pink grapefruit vodka, shaken with honey. It arrives with Licor 43 and lemon, chilled with a supersized atom lolly–quite funky–alongside his Singapore Sling.

He's jokingly enacting a role-play scene, with him playing a male escort, looking suave in his misty grey waistcoat, crisp white shirt and matching grey suit pants.

"Hello, darling, I'm your escort for tonight."

I have to giggle, trying to stay relaxed. "You're such a joker."

"Why? Don't you fancy me?"

"You know I fancy you, but I don't like the thought of you being an escort."

"Why?" Shit, is he doing this because he thinks I'm an escort?

"I want you all to myself." I don't miss a beat.

He is hot. Fitter than any guy I've dated in the past. His tropical-blue eyes, his short, curly, acorn-brown hair and oversized lips absolutely do it for me. Even his teeth are perfectly straight, gleaming pearly white whenever he smiles. All the waitresses' eyes cling to him. They want a piece of him.

He's made it clear that we're in a relationship now, and that I mustn't cheat. He wants me all to himself.

I took on the Cat persona long before we became serious, well before we got together. I sleep with other men because it's my job, it's how I earn money to survive and to pay the bills, nothing more. Does that make me a worse person or a better person?

What he doesn't know won't hurt him.

"When are you next working?" he asks casually. He thinks I work for a city centre department store, as a floor manager still, staying behind late for extra pocket money.

"Tuesday."

"I'll pick you up after."

What the fuck? What do I say to avoid him picking me up from work? Is he suspicious?

"Well, I drive myself to work. I'm not going to leave my car stranded."

"Get your mum to drop you off at work and I'll collect. Simple."

"Why are you so eager to pick me up from work? Do you not like me working alongside other men?"

"If you work where you say you work then there should be no issue with me collecting you."

"Collect me then, I'm not bothered." I call his bluff, trying to throw him off my scent.

"Great. I'll finish work early on Tuesday and pick you up, then we can go out for dinner."

"Sure." I go along with his plans. I have to create an escape route, make up an excuse to avoid him on Tuesday. The sick feeling in my gut tells me that he's on to me. The sickness is worse than the thought of any money worries hanging over my head, and poverty was the only reason I began selling myself in the first place.

Tuesday arrives. I feel terrible, but I've come in to work. I can't simply not turn up, because the boss is strict, and I already have clients who've made reservations. She could sack me if she believes I'm not reliable. In between bookings I'm thinking of an excuse to give Mr Gold about why he can't come and get me.

"Hey, honey, nice to see you again," I greet my regular client, Adam. He's in his twenties, has his own distribution business and can afford to pay me for sex weekly.

"Yeah, babes, likewise, I've not seen you in a few weeks. It's the end of Ramadan today, so that's why I'm here."

"Oh, is it party time tonight then?"

"Yes, I've finished work early today so I can celebrate Eid with my family."

Bingo! I can tell Mr Gold it's Eid today for the Muslims in my workplace, so work is closing two hours early, but I'll have to ask the boss if I can leave work early too.

Mr Gold messages me at three o'clock:

Hey, beautiful. Message me the address of your work and I'll collect you. Looking forward to picking you up. X

I ignore him. He messages me again at three-thirty:

Hey, beautiful, did you get my last text? Where am I collecting you from? X

Yes, I did get your message. I've just been really busy today. I can't keep messaging you whilst I'm in work. I will be back at my mum's house about 9.30 pm if you want to collect me from there? X

No. I'll come and pick you up from work, Baby. X

I ignore his message.

So?

He messages me again at five:

???

"Please can I leave at seven?" I ask the receptionist. "My boyfriend is demanding to pick me up from work. He thinks I work at some department store. I don't know what to do. Can you tell the boss I have to leave in an emergency? I haven't messaged him back."

"Yes of course, Cat."

I chuck my wages and lingerie inside my work bag. I change into some normal-looking clothes and say a few quick goodbyes to the staff. As I scurry out of the building, I'm anxious in case he's hanging around outside the premises. I throw my work bag into the boot of my car then connect my mobile to my car's Bluetooth. I reverse my car out of the tight parking space and dial Mr Gold's phone number as I'm driving off. His phone rings.

"Hi, beautiful, I was getting worried that you wouldn't tell me where it is I'm picking you up from. But now you've phoned. . ."

I butt in, "Yes, about that. I've left work early. It's Eid, you see."

"What? Where are you now then?"

"On my way back home. I'm driving."

"But you knew I was picking you up. Why would you drive your car to work? Something strange is going on!" His voice is rising in tone. "Where are you now? Why won't you let me pick you up from work? Where is it that you work? Tell me now?"

"What's your problem? Why are you being weird?"

"I don't believe you anymore. If you won't let me pick you up, it proves you have something to hide. It's over!"

"What? I have nothing to. . ."

He slams the phone down on me. I redial his number in a panic. I don't want our relationship to die.

"What? What do you want? I knew you would do this to me. All you had to do was let me pick you up to ease my mind. And you can't even do that. You're hiding something from me. I know it! Do you think I'm dumb? Do you think I'll put up with you being sly?"

"Sly? What are you talking about? I'm not being sly."

"Yes, you are! If you can't, for some unknown reason, let me pick you up from your secret workplace then it's over." He ends the call again.

No. I don't want it to be over. I need him in my life. I was beginning to fall for him. Painful heartache runs through my body. I want our relationship to work. I phone him again.

"Hello. . . Please let me explain."

"Why? So, you can tell me another lie? No way."

"Do you love me? If you love me then you'll let me explain."

"I'm driving home," he says. "You can explain to me face-to-face why you won't let me pick you up." He hangs up for the third time.

Shit! Fuck! Shit! What do I tell him? What believable excuse can I give him? Where do I say I've been working? I phone my mother.

"Mum. He's going crazy after I didn't let him pick me up from work. He's driving home to confront me."

"Tell him your boss is strict. Tell him that's why you can't let him pick you up."

"No, Mum. It won't work. Where can I say I've been working?"

"Okay, tell him you thought he'd be pissed off if he saw you working for a rich guy."

"Do you think that will work?"

"Yes."

"Thank you. I'm nearly at his house now. Bye."

"Bye."

My heart is in my mouth. I hope this excuse is plausible or he'll leave me for sure.

I see his car parked up on his driveway. He's perched on the bonnet with his arms crossed.

"Do you want me to come inside?" I ask.

"Yes, if you're going to tell me the truth."

"Look, I will tell you, but promise me you won't be mad at me for hiding some things from you."

"I won't." His voice is calmer now. "What have you been hiding from me, exactly?"

"Well. . . You know I told you I've been working at a department store? Well, I thought you'd start an argument with the director if you saw him because he's actually quite young and good-looking. I thought you'd make me lose my job. I've not told my boss I'm in a relationship, you see. I know you'd be jealous of me working with him. I just know."

"I wouldn't be jealous."

"Yes, you would. You know you would. Look how weird you're being now."

"Is that the truth?"

"Yes. I didn't want you to collect me from there in case you'd get me the sack; you know how you kick off."

"Is that all it is? Truly?"

"Yes. Now can I come inside, or is it over like you said it was before?"

"Come here. Give me a hug."

"No, I don't want to hug you. I can't believe you could so easily end our relationship when I've done nothing wrong." I walk away from him. "You act as though I mean nothing to you." I open his front door and leave it ajar.

"Oh, baby, I'm sorry. I didn't mean it. You know I love you." He traipses behind me, closing the door.

"Well, if you love me, then you should trust me. It's because you are so jealous in nature that I felt I had to hide where I work from you. I'll tell my boss he can find someone else instead of me from now on." There, I've just turned the argument back around on him.

"Look, I don't want you to be working for a man I don't even know. He could be a pervert or anything." He's being controlling now.

"I'll tell my boss tomorrow."

Relief! The excuse has worked, I think. I've won him over, or is it because he loves me that he's let me off the hook? I have to be realistic; I'm not going to get away this lightly again. Something is going to have to change.

"Mm. . . I'm rock hard for you." He places my hand upon his crotch.

I kiss him in return.

He kisses me back aggressively, pulling my vest top up to reveal my bra. I pull down my black leather pencil skirt. He unzips his trousers and drops them to the floor, and then takes down his briefs. I wrap my hand around his hard-on. He twists my body around to face away from him and unclasps my bra, exposing my breasts.

"Bend over. Let me have a piece of you."

I allow him to bend me over and pull my lace thong down

over my buttocks. As it falls to my ankles, he glides himself inside me, thrusting harder and harder.

"Yes. Yes," I moan.

"I'm so fucking horny. I want to finish off deep inside you." He has never mentioned finishing off inside me before. Is this his way of showing me I fulfil his needs as a woman? He wants me to be his. He wants us to have a future together, to make a family.

He keeps thrusting into me. I lose track of time. I can feel an orgasm building up.

"Yes. Yes. I'm going to orgasm. Oh. Yes." I let him know he's satisfying me.

"Can I finish inside you, baby?"

"Yes."

"Oh! Oh! Yes. Shit, that is the best!" he pushes himself inside me the furthest it can reach, and then slowly slides himself back out.

All thoughts of working as a call-girl have vanished from my mind. I want to make our relationship work. Will I ever again walk out of the changing room at work and walk over to the reception desk, dressed in lingerie, and peer down at my booking sheet from behind the desk to see which gentleman is waiting for my attention? If not, there is a bit of me that is going to miss the place.

A message I get soon after from a cat friend melts my heart:

I just want to say, thank you for being you! You have kind of 'broken the mould' with cat caring. You are a glamorous, lovely lady who is changing the perception that cat lovers are lonely, ageing grannies! You are gorgeous inside and out. God bless you, thank you for what you do.

CHAPTER TWENTY-ONE

Two weeks and six days. That's how long I've booked to be in Sydney, Australia. I've wanted to go since I first heard the world's finest short-stay boutique hotel and brothel exists there. And I can earn enough there to support myself and as many cats as I plan to for quite some time without Mr Gold asking to collect me from work.

Adonis, my brother, is pretty much my right arm concerning this plan of mine: booking our flights, selecting a reasonably-priced hotel in close proximity to Platinum Heels. He is the brains behind my master plan. Adonis has never judged me regarding my occupation.

I have to start thinking of quicker ways to earn money to support all these cats and live my life the way I know how to. Well, not that I always want to be touched by all the men who hire me, now I'm dating Mr Gold, but now I've had the taste for dirty money, no other job tastes as sweet. Oh, and about Mr Gold: I didn't give him too much of an explanation as to this holiday, just told him my brother had a spare ticket because his now ex-girlfriend had pulled out, and I didn't want him to go abroad alone. I'll decide what I want to do with our relationship when I get back, whether or not to confess.

The flights consume a full day of my time. Time means money. I'm not even sure if I'll have a job when we get there.

"Good morning, Platinum Heels, how may I help?" The telephone operator reels off her well-practised words.

"Hi. I was told to ring for an interview as soon as I landed in Sydney."

"No problem, your name?"

"Cat."

"Great. Shall we say eleven o'clock?"

"Eleven this morning?"

"Yes."

Oh heck. That's only an hour away. I must look exhausted from the thirty-hour journey, but I suppose it's just an interview, and nothing a touch of make-up can't fix. "That's fine," I say. "See you at eleven."

The hotel is pretty cheap. If I'm going to make money on this trip I have to spend wisely. Plus, not even knowing whether I have a job is quite daunting. I probably need to earn at least £6,000 before I make any money to call my own. Plus, Adonis is only a teenager, and I do recall saying I would treat him if he came with me.

"Adonis, I have to go to the interview in an hour. Can you come with me and wait outside? I don't know where it is."

"Sure. I looked on Google Earth before we came." Genius. He has a head full of knowledge. He knows exactly where Platinum Heels is now; he's been scouring the area online.

"I know, but I'm no good at things like that. I'll get lost."

"It's one straight road. You won't get lost, but I'll come with you anyway. I can have a cigarette while I wait."

"Do you have to smoke? I hate it when you smoke." I care about him. He's like my little baby, even though he's taller than me these days.

"I'm going to try and cut down while we're here."

Beep. Beep. The sound of a car horn as we walk.

"Did you see that guy?" Adonis says. "He couldn't keep his eyes off you. And the other one, beeping."

"Yes, it's annoying."

"Can't be a bad thing."

"Suppose you're right, I just think it's rude to beep at a woman in public. Blokes beep from behind sometimes, when they haven't even seen my face."

Because I fuck for a living, you wouldn't think I'd be bothered by the beeping of a horn. You might think I'd lift my top up and flash my tits or drop my panties, but no. In the 'real world' I have a lot of respect for myself—and I play hard to get.

I can't help but get nervous as we approach the entrance. Red sultry lips painted on the grey wash wall. To me, this marks sex appeal. We've hit the right place.

From the exterior, this set-up is similar to work back in England. Cameras. Heavy, safeguarded door. Buzzer. At least I know it's secure—well, it seems to be.

I shake hands with a beautiful, long-legged, long-haired blonde, wearing all black—casual but sexy business attire.

"Esmeralda will be here soon. I can carry out your interview, though. Follow me to the bar area."

This is a mansion above all mansions, telling me I should

know which side my bread is buttered. This place screams 'there's money to be made'. Tottering past the colossal crystal chandelier and the red-carpeted, aluminium spiral staircase, we head towards the curtained-off bar area. A welcoming sight. There's a corner seating area in purple and silver. She pulls the curtains closed for privacy—whose privacy? Mine? The punters? The other working girls? Then, she re-appears behind the bar.

"Take a seat, make yourself comfortable." She is stern, but sexy with it. I wonder if she does what I came here to do? Not in that business-like attire, I suspect—bar the breakneck heels. "Would you like a drink?"

"No, thank you." I've had enough free beverages on the plane to satisfy my need for liquids for at least a day.

"Here's a pen. Fill in both sides of the interview form, back and front." She hands me a clipboard and biro. "I'll leave you to it. It may take a while." Her perfectly rounded eyes gaze into mine. She's striking. I bet she catches plenty of attention in here.

Interview Form

Please answer Yes or No to the following questions and fill in more details where necessary.

Real name: XXXXXX

Name you wish to be known by: Cat.

Age: 28.

Age you wish to have on Platinum Heels website: 27.

Breast size: 30EE.

Natural breasts: No.

Dress size: 10 UK.

Shaven, Brazilian: Shaven.

Shoe size: 5.

Eye colour: Hazel.

Hair colour: Brunette.

Skin tone: Olive.

Bisexual: Yes.

Would you participate in a lesbian scene: Yes.

Would you have an orgy: Yes.

Would you have a long stay booking: Yes.

Personality: Playful, sexy and seductive.

Party girl: Yes.

Do you drink alcohol: Yes.

Sexual health checked in last 3 weeks: Yes.

Certificate of sexual health: Will go to the sexual health clinic.

Start date: ASAP.

Willing List: OW, GFE, role-play, RA, foot worship, toy-show, kissing, domination, dress-up, protected sex, watersports, fetishes.

Smoker: No.

Flexibility hours: Any.

Flexible on days: Sunday to Saturday.

Country from: England.

Where have you worked before: High-class parlour in Manchester, UK.

Out-calls: No.

Tattoos: No.

Body piercings: No.

Languages spoken: English.

Rented accommodation in Platinum Heels: No.

Phone Number: XXXXXXX

Email: XXXXXXX

Address: XXXXXXXX

Passport or driving licence ID: Yes.

How long will you be staying in Australia: Two weeks and six days.

How did you hear about Platinum Heels: Word of mouth.

Do you know anyone who works here: No.

N.B: Natural services are prohibited. Anyone found offering natural services will be dismissed.

Stockings must be worn at Platinum Heels at all times. Anyone not wearing stockings will be fined $50.

Warning: All Platinum Heels ladies are advised not to take or give contact numbers away. This will result in dismissal.

Please note: Provided information will be placed on the Platinum Heels website for customers to view apart from confidential details.

Ladies are not permitted to work on the premises without a Certificate Of Sexual Health.

What the heck are 'Natural Services'? And why do they ask if I'm a 'Party girl'? I do like to socialise, so I answered 'yes', but I'm going to have to query it with Esmeralda. I'm not overly keen on the thought of attending a party in a foreign country, stranded in unfamiliar territory.

Seventeen minutes she's been gone for. Adonis is waiting for me. What a joke. I knew filling in this form wouldn't 'take a while'. Maybe some girls have to take a while deciding whether they are inclined to an orgy, or whether they are in fact bisexual or not. Maybe they're just not quite sure of the undercover name they wish to use. Of course, I have been tested at the sexual health clinic in England, I have a boyfriend, and I'm cautious. Surely a clinic over here will allow me to take another sexual health screening.

No mention of whether I have a criminal record, as other interviews would. As for my real name, that's always a touchy subject, but I'm counting on this job, so I conform. There. I see her, as I poke my head through the curtains, past the purple and red shaded walkways, past the trickled spotlit water flow trailing near the ruffled floor-to-ceiling entrance curtains. What's she playing at? Hello? Has she forgotten about me in the bar area already? I'm not waiting any longer—it's unfair on Adonis, waiting all alone outside a brothel.

"I've finished the form." I'm ready to leave. I'm not having anyone taking the piss. I'm ready to walk. She takes the form and glances at it. I'm not embarrassed. Obviously, I said 'yes' to participating in lesbian scenes and 'yes' to bisexual, even though I'm not at all bisexual—I just said that to be appealing.

"Cat. Hmm. Is that what you wish to be called?"

"Yes."

"Another lady is called Cat here."

"Really?" What a coincidence.

"I'm afraid you will have to go by another name."

"Xena?"

"Nope, holding her left hand on her hip, with the clipboard in her right hand, "That name has been taken too."

"Polly?" This is harder than I thought. How many girls entertain here? They're taking all my names.

"Lacey?"

"Another. We have a Lacey here already." This time her pen is between her teeth. For fuck's sake.

"Penelope?"

"Not sure about that one."

What? Not sure? What's not to be sure about that name?

"I don't know then. It's hard to pluck a name out of thin air, on the spot."

"Dolly. I quite like Dolly for you."

"Dolly?" I jest.

"It suits you. Yeah." Shining her perfectly lined teeth.

"Dolly it is then."

We shake on it.

"How about stayin' for a while?"

"Now?"

"No time like the present."

"I've only just landed off the plane." I'm exhausted. I need the money though. "If I could go back to the hotel, unpack, and bring a few outfits I should be okay. . . My brother is outside waiting for me, you see."

*

I took a shopping trip a few hours before my flight. New bras, panties, stockings, the lot, all packed in my brother's case.

"Perfect. I'll roster you in."

"May I ask how long the shifts are?"

"It's a trial. There are no fixed hours on a trial. You can stay as long as you like, however I would advise you staying for five hours or so." Of course she would; the more hours I sell my body for, the higher the fee Platinum Heels banks.

"Okay, great." Swivelling to the left, throwing my hair to the right side of my shoulder, I see a shadow of someone lurking in the backdrop on the right, four curtains down, past the spot lit water flow. Is someone following me? Why am I so tense? For heaven's sake, you're not in England, pick yourself up and stop with the paranoia.

"You'll do well here."

"You think?" I wet my lips with the tip of my tongue.

"Sure do. Pretty little thing like yourself." Her eyes drift onto the tassels of my new beige cowgirl coat, past my black, low-cut dress, then down my oiled legs to my matching beige cowgirl ankle boots, and back up to my eyes. I wonder if she'll insist on sneaking a peek of my embroidered underwear next? Is she coming on to me, or does she know I'm good for it? Good for the game, that is.

"Thanks." Confidence boosted.

"Good luck, I won't be here when you're back. My shift ends then."

"See you soon." Taking a step away. "Oh, before I forget, the form mentioned having a certificate of sexual health, and, as I'm new to Sydney, how do I go about getting one? Obviously, I've had the all-clear over in England."

"No problem. The clinic is literally two minutes away in Camperdown. . . Esmerelda." The blonde nods in greeting to the lady who apparently should have taken my interview.

"Who do we have here?" Esmeralda bends her head towards me. A mousy blonde, mid-forties I'd say, beautiful curves.

"Dolly. Well, Cat in the email. Dolly in the flesh."

"Dolly?"

"Yes," I say. "She chose Dolly for me."

"Not sure about Dolly," Esmeralda's face is puzzled, eyes slightly squinting.

"I like Dolly," The long-legged blonde sniffs.

"Do you?" Esmeralda pierces me with her eyes.

"Truthfully?" I pause, whilst my eyes flick from left to right at each lady. "I'm not sure." I don't want to sound too ungrateful. "I don't mind, whatever name."

"Dolly is good for marketing," the blonde lets loose.

"Have a think about it," Esmeralda gives me an option.

I wonder who's the more senior of these two?

"I'll buzz you out." The blonde presses the door release button.

*

It's not long before Adonis and I have unpacked, and I've reloaded my sex-on-wheels case. Stockings of various shades, heels, two pairs apiece for matching outfits, thirty condoms—I'm sure Platinum Heels will have more on sale if needs be. Thigh-high, high-heeled, crushed-suede boots crammed in. Tartan red and black stripy schoolgirl role-play set. Angelic white lace weaved panties, push-up bra, garter and socks. My favourite lilac and fuchsia three-piece, and a black sparkly sequined boob-tube dress for a sophisticated look, in case there's a party. Ready to roll.

"I feel bad leaving you, though," I tell Adonis.

"I'll be fine. I'll go to the bar, walk to get something to eat on Parramatta Road, watch a film on the laptop, sleep."

"Okay. If you need me call me on the pay-as-you-go phone or ask for me at work."

I know asking my eighteen-year-old brother to take me to or collect me from a brothel is crazy, but he's cool.

"Thanks for being here with me. I'll call you later, when my trial ends, then you can meet me back here. Oh, and can you tell mum to make sure the cat huts are all filled with straw and not wet? It may be summer here, but it's winter in England."

*

"When you greet him, shake his hand and sit beside him, if you like. Tell him your name." Esmeralda tells me before my first introductory meeting. She knows my experience. She knows I've fucked for a living in England. "Open the curtains on entry and close them on exit for discreetness. Clients here are given the utmost privacy. There must be no clients bumping into each other or being in view of one another."

I straighten up my black sparkly sequined boob-tube dress, neatening my stockings the second Esmeralda's back was turned.

Drawing aside the weighty mauve velvet drape, I shuffle in. "Hello there."

"Hi. I asked to see you." Irish accent. Porcelain skinned, ash brown to blond hair, slight physique, seasonal blue checks and stripes on his unbuttoned shirt, tee underneath. A bulky rucksack beside the midpoint glass table.

"Glad you did, nice to meet you," I say sitting beside him, placing my hand tenderly on his lap. "My name is Dolly."

"Dilly?"

"No, Dolly, not Dilly," I laugh, lightly stroking the crease of his beige chino trousers near his crotch, but not fully—he hasn't reserved me yet.

"That's nice." What's nice, my name or my hand on his leg? His hand presses my soft touch harder on his package. Hard-on already.

"You have questions for me?" Removing my hand but flashing my teeth in a cheeky smile—obviously I want the booking.

"What would you do in the room and what wouldn't you do?"

"There's not much I wouldn't do. I love having fun."

His hand moves mine up and down on his penis.

"I'm not supposed to do this, I could get in trouble. Have me in the room and I'll show you a good time." I stand tall. No one's told me if this hanky-panky is permitted during the welcoming, but I'm guessing a place like this would boot him out if I grassed.

"Will you deep throat?"

"Mm, yes."

"Don't go yet."

"What do you mean?"

I'm not staying in here all night with him. He takes hold of my wrist.

Twisting left to right, out of his grasp. "I have to go, darling,"

I step backwards. "A lady is waiting to give me a Platinum Heels tour." A quick get-out excuse.

Shifting the drapes at either side, I lift my oiled legs over the ruffled bottom half of the curtain.

"Bye."

Mood lights of lilac, crimson and pink create an ambiance in the antechambers as I get my bearings on the walkway by the front desk. This place is a maze. Already I've taken a wrong turn. Fuck. I can't be getting sacked yet. There are 'no entry' signs on display, doors labelled D, E, F, G, H, I, J. Where the hell am I? What goes on in these rooms? Why no entry? No entry for clients, or for me?

"Tour?" I mouth as I head closer to Esmeralda. Bet she saw me heading off-track on the cameras.

"Off we go." She leads the way under the colossal crystal chandelier. "We haven't got long, usually there would be more time for sightseeing but there's a gentleman in room A who wants to book you. He's waiting for you. We'll have to rush."

Great—being hurried isn't a thing of mine.

'He wants me? That was quick." I've hardly got my bum warm. The crotch-touching worked a treat. "This place is remarkable." I'm in heaven.

"It is. Girls from all over the world travel to work here: Poland, Brazil, Spain, Thailand, Malaysia, Scotland, Mexico."

"Multicultural. How interesting."

"The word gets around. Some stay for a couple of weeks, others months, others years. You're beautiful, you'll fit in well."

"Thanks."

We come to a door. Club69, one of the luxury suites here,

she closes the door behind us for privacy. Jacuzzi water plunge pool, personal bar, unlimited refreshments in the refrigerator, shower and toilet in each room. "Here," she points at a gadget on the wall, "are eight music buttons to choose from; you create your mood."

"Cool." Blimey, this place sure raises the bar, it must have cost a fortune. I'd like to own a place like this one day.

"Pole. . . if you have time." She has humour.

"Loving the disco ball under the spotlights."

"Each suite has its own theme."

"Will I be in this room?"

"At the moment you can choose, depending on if the room is free. Ask one of the team which room you're in when you're taking your client up the staircase. Always enter up the front staircase and exit out the back."

"Bedsheets are cleaned after each appointment."

"Sure."

"Anything you want to ask?"

"Yes. Is there a clock anywhere? Usually when the service is nearly over, I like to know. Men just want all the time in the world when they're in the heat of the moment, but I don't like to run over on time."

"Oh, don't worry about that, five minutes before the end you will hear a buzz from the internal system, here on the wall," she signals with her forefinger. "The cashier at the desk upstairs deals with that side of the business. You tell her when you're about to start the service, unless you're ready to leave for the day. You can buzz on this button here, no need to shout, it's very sensitive to sound." So, I take it whoever is on the receiving end will hear me shagging—no problem.

"Different to the last brothel I worked in. I'll have to keep reminding myself to buzz out then, if I'm not naked."

"It's okay to wrap a towel around you if needs be, say, if you need to extend time further, if the client wants more time. If you don't, you run the risk of clients bumping into each other, which is against the rules. Discretion is of the highest order here; it's what we pride ourselves on. There can be no clients bumping into other clients, ever. So, when you're on your way out, buzz, and you will be told if the coast is clear."

"Got it."

Every door is named, she re-opens Club69's heavy timber door, gesturing to the silver alphabet and numerical title.

"Can the girls use the jacuzzi when desired?"

"On a two-hour booking only—anything less, no."

"Do I ask for permission if it's a two-hour booking, or more?"

"On the buzzer, yes. All you do is. . ." she leads me to the toilet. Strange. What could be in the lavatory? "Button one at the top is to fill the water, button two is to set the jets off," she makes her way to the jacuzzi, bending over. "When you're done it's your responsibility to empty it." Giving me a lesson, pulling the plug, then placing it back in. "Air conditioning is controlled from within the room also. Any problems, let a member of the team know, it's pretty straightforward though, plus and minus for hotter or lower."

"Do I pay a set fee at the end of the shift?"

"What happens is we take a fee off each client from the money he gives you, or off his card at the desk upstairs. At the end of the shift your fee is deducted, the cashier holds all the money, any tips are yours for the keeping but best to give all money to the cashier."

Roman Orgy—loving the sound of this room. Betty Boob—fair dos. Kama Sutra—now we're talking. Red padded headboard, long liqueur-filled bar. Can't wait to get a shot of whatever tickles my fancy.

"Hello Monique, new lady here." Esmeralda introduces me. "This is where you go after you've seen your client to the designated room. You bring the payment here, Monique or another cashier fills out your sheet of appointments and any extras or tips you receive." Into the backroom she goes, me following. "This is where you fill your bucket with ice," she pulls out a stainless-steel deluxe ice bucket and fills it with ice, then chucks it back onto the ice maker, ready for the next girl. "More refreshments are in this fridge, they're replenished frequently, if you need any." Very helpful, indeed, the more drinks the merrier the guest.

"Hi, Monique, do you have a stock of condoms?"

"Of course. We're a brothel." Monique's Eastern European accent is harsh, she pulls a sarcastic face. Step down, bitch—I needed to fucking know.

Esmeralda steps in. "There's always someone here, condoms are in the bottom drawer; large, small, medium, thin textured, flavoured—the works."

"I have my own for now, I was just curious." I dagger at Monique. I have to be careful what I say because I'm new and I'm working under her.

"Understandable. We run a strict policy." No 'natural services'. So that's what it means.

I nod; time is of the essence here. I need the money off this client. This is what I came for—isn't it?

"When you exit the booking it's important you don't forget

to hand your money to the cashier. Put your clutch bag in this cabinet along with all the others." Esmeralda opens a sliding door to demonstrate tones of metallic pink, red, black, silver, gold, glittery, leopard print, tartan, PVC.

"Okay." It's a lot to take in, but nonetheless I nod again, looking like I know the drill. Buzz in, buzz out, buzz, buzz, blah, blah.

"These are only some of the rooms, the others are on the next level up, for a longer stay usually, longer bookings. Some clients stay all night, all day, days at a time some of them."

Bonking hell! Days at a time? Not sure if I could do that, not even on a high-energy beverage.

"Is kissing forbidden?" Still curious—it seems I'm in a new world here.

"You can kiss if you like, that's at your discretion. Some of the girls charge extra for kissing, some don't, I think it depends on whether they feel comfortable with the man or if it's their regular client."

I follow her into the James Bond room, whilst what looks at first sight like a couple, hand-in-hand, passes by, the man eyeing me up.

"In each room there's a seat, a moveable torch attached to the wall and a switch. Before agreeing anything, you must inspect the client." Hang on, inspect? Come again? "Take a close look at their genitals—the light is bright, and if you're not happy with any marks, if they are not noticeably clean, any funny smells, abandon them. Tell them you don't wish to see them and tell them to wait while you inform the team." How embarrassing, but how cool. "Now, the back entrance is this way."

We walk past more doors, some open, some closed. The walkways are long. Cleaners are out with catering trolleys full of clean, crisply folded white towels, bed sheets, carrier bags for the condom bins, mops, brushes, dustpans.

I've had the tour; the place looks great and now I'm all set up for my first client. I make my way to the Presidential Suite and open the door.

CHAPTER TWENTY-TWO

"You're my love," Mr Gold skims his thumb over my cheek-bone.

I feel a frisson. He's taking me to Mauritius on holiday only one week after landing home from Sydney. Mother is caring for the colony cats for me whilst I'm away.

"I've missed you."

"I've missed you too," I am swept away, seized in this moment. He's kept the exact location of the hotel hidden, keeping me intrigued.

The flight is long. We eventually arrive at the jungle-themed, six-star spa resort. The complex resembles a desert island. It's called the Palace Hotel, an embarrassing coincidence—or is Mr Gold letting me know he knows all about my working life? The hotel is located on a tropical coastline amidst skyscraper palm trees and the lobby has a sandy floor. Wooden decking areas wind through gardens and there is the potent smell of lavender seeping from the spa into the warm air.

The bar is called the Palace Bar, the restaurant the Palace Restaurant. The lounge is called. . . you guessed it. What the hell? I can't escape, there's nowhere to run and we're trapped here together, so I'll try to keep calm. He's all I have for company in this resort. I'm blissful at this thought, but also scared in case he's brought me here to shame me.

"What's he looking at?" Mr Gold glowers at another guest in the restaurant, who seems to be staring at me.

"Nothing."

"He'd better take his eyes off you now or I'll remove them."

"Leave it. It's okay. I'm with you."

"And he knows it. He can see you're with me, so why's he staring at you?"

I kiss him. The holidaymaker walks away and Mr Gold calms down.

After dinner we take cocktails back to our suite. Before we even have time to sip them, he's slipping down my dress. He rests naked on top of my body, crossing my ankles in the air, my legs in the star-crossed position as I lay on the bed. He raises my buttocks and slides himself in and out of me slowly, kissing my lips lovingly as I leverage myself to meet his thrusts. The rapture is phenomenal. He and I are here together making love, away from all of life's worries and anguish. Pleasing each other is all we care about tonight.

He presses my breasts to his chest. We are touching foreheads and gazing into one another's eyes as he erupts.

The sound of sexual moaning has been replaced by the light blowing of the air conditioning unit and the distant thrashing of the Indian Ocean on the rocks at the rear of the hotel. There's no other place I'd rather be. If tonight was to be the last night of our lives, I'd be content to spend it in his arms.

"I love you. Sweet dreams, beautiful," he whispers into my ear.

I roll over. "Love you too. Night."

The sunrise shines through our hotel curtains.

"Carpe diem. Let's seize the day, beautiful." He lifts his naked body out of the bed and sweeps the curtains open.

I'm booked into the spa for a massage. Hopefully it's a female masseuse. I'd say no to a man massaging me here because Mr Gold would get jealous. I wear a white cotton kaftan with a white bikini set, which crosses diagonally over my breasts, my cleavage showing at the edges, and black oval sunglasses. At least it's not called the Palace Spa.

"Hello. Can I help you, madam? Do you have an appointment?" the spa receptionist asks. Her words sound familiar, the sort of words used to greet clients at the Palace Lounge.

I feel like royalty. Maybe this is how clients at my work feel—pampered. I feel majestic as she opens doors for me. The masseuse leads me into a peaceful, jasmine-scented, bamboo-walled room. Relaxing music fills the air. She's laid the spa treatment bed out ready for me and passes me a tall glass of bubbling Champagne.

I neck the Champagne in three swift gulps, pulling down my clothes quickly. The spa room is on a cream sandy beach and through the window I'm overlooking the Indian Ocean. Deep red and pink tropical flowers are scattered everywhere.

Closing my eyes, allowing my body to unwind, I'm ready for her to take over my senses. She begins to massage and in a strange way it turns me on. Now I know why the men I massage get aroused at the traces of my fingers upon their skin. My muscles relax, allowing me to drift away.

"How long will she be?"

I hear Mr Gold's voice coming from the spa foyer. I don't exactly know how long I've been receiving a massage for as I drifted off.

"Did you enjoy?" The masseuse asks.

"Yes, thank you," I feel sleepy and relaxed.

"She very beautiful lady." A spa lady smiles and looks at Mr Gold as I come out, then back at me, then back at him.

"Yes, I know. Thank you. I'm a lucky man."

We're both lucky to be here in paradise. My lips meet his for a tender kiss.

We stroll to the beach for a barbeque. Mr Gold sits beside me on a sun-warmed bench. I can sense he wants to be near to me, which makes me feel exultant. As we tuck into our chargrilled food, my phone bleeps. I reach into my beach bag and unlock my handset in front of him, not realising he's looking over my shoulder. A picture appears from an old work colleague of a missing prostitute. I scroll down to read the newspaper caption.

"What's that?" his expression has darkened.

I panic and instantly shut my screen off. "Nothing."

"Nothing? It didn't look like nothing to me."

"It was just a picture message off my friend, that's all." I become frantic, trying to hide my nervousness and carry on eating.

"Show it to me then, if it's nothing."

"Okay. It's a newspaper article about a missing girl, that's all." I hold my phone towards him.

"Let me read it." He snatches the phone from my grasp. "This isn't about a normal girl going missing, it's about a fucking prostitute."

"No, it's not." Trying to hide my fear.

"Why are you receiving that type of message from a friend? It's as though she's warning other prostitutes." He leans his head downwards in his bicep and takes in a deep breath.

"No, it's not like that at all. Sometimes my friends send me internet links and pictures of shocking newspaper stories."

"Yeah. Yeah. Whatever you say." He picks up his plate and moves to another bench.

"What are you accusing me of?"

"You know what."

"No. I don't."

"What is it you actually do for a living then?"

"What? You know I'm a retail manager. Or, I was, before you wanted me to quit."

"Well, go on then, remind me what your work involved."

"Stop it; your arguing is putting me off my food."

"There's loads of unanswered questions with you. Who paid for your fake tits? How did you afford them?"

"Who do you think you are asking me personal questions about my body? If I choose to have a breast augmentation that's my decision."

"It doesn't add up. The jigsaw pieces don't fit."

"If you wanted cosmetic surgery, I wouldn't interfere."

"All right then, forget it."

"You really ought to think sometimes before you speak. I'm really uncomfortable now about my breasts. You've upset me. I'm not going on any excursions with you today. Forget it." I turn the argument around on him.

"Sorry, I didn't mean to upset you."

The waiter spots the tension as he approaches to refill our beverages.

"Everything alright here? Would you like some fresh drinks?"

"A triple Hennessy brandy and cola," Mr Gold snaps.

"Can I have a double Malibu and cola, please?"

We leave the picnic bench and carry our drinks with us to the sand, sitting down, side-by-side on sun loungers.

"Will you put some sun cream on my back?" He seems to be trying to make amends. I want to make things right too.

I apply factor twenty lightly on his back and on my own skin, then lay back and open a book. I feel stressed out by our argument.

I receive a text message from my sister:

Hi, sis, I hope you are both having a lovely time away. I've decided to remove myself from the BPTC course before they make me pay the £17,000 in fees. My heart's not in it anymore. It'll take years for me to work my way up in the law industry, paying for pupillage shadowing a barrister, then being on the minimum wage until I'm possibly scouted by a decent law firm. And if I don't cut off all my hair, who knows, I may never be scouted. I don't feel comfortable with you working to fund my living expenses so I can study. I see how happy you are being with Mr Gold too. You both bring out the best in each other, and that makes me smile. You beam with happiness when you speak of him. I know you always try to sway me on this topic, but I feel I'm a grown woman now, not your little sister who you always try to protect. I know you love me and want what's best for me in life, so you need to trust me that this is

*what I want for my future. I'll be forever grateful for you helping
me get this far. I want to have a career in something that makes
me happy. I love you.*
Take lots of pictures whilst you are away. Keep safe. X

Wow. So, I don't have to pay £17,000 for the BPTC she needs.
Like she said it'll take years for her to work her way up in the
law industry, probably shadowing a barrister and then on
minimum wage until she's scouted. Then I'd be struggling
financially for years to come if I didn't carry on selling my
body.

I feel a huge weight is lifted off my shoulders. I feel guilty
about my work now and I don't want to hurt Gold. I truly
don't want to cheat on him. If I stop paying for my sister's
studying, as she's pleading me to, then there's no urgency
anymore to sell myself to fund it, and Mr Gold and I can
pursue our relationship. I have different priorities now. My
sister understands. Her heart's not seemingly into the law
profession anymore. But how will I feed and care for the sixty
plus colony cats if I revert back to a minimum wage salary
packet? The cats depend on me. How will I reach the dream
of building a feral and stray cat sanctuary?

By the time Mr Gold and I land back on English soil
all I can think about is heading straight for the superstore
to buy treats for the colony cats, even though that'll be at a
cost. I feel as though I've become as dependent on his love
as I am on the money I earn. Since choosing a different path
to being a high-class call girl, I've got a new dream now that
will justify what I used to do for money: helping the cats
survive.

EPILOGUE

So that's that, dear reader. My secret is out. I'm back from my Antipodean adventure and I am looking to lead a quiet and uneventful life with the love of my life and my beautiful cats. I will continue to save as many stray and feral cats as I can and live in hope of building a safe haven for them.

That's the reason why I've finally decided to reveal my secret to highlight the plight of the cats that need help, and to encourage others to do whatever they can in their communities. Feral cats may be unloved by some, but they are just as deserving of the love and of protection that we humans can give them.

If one cat finds a new, love-filled life as a result of me revealing my secret. . . My story will have been totally worth it.

Best whiskers,
Cat

ABOUT THE AUTHOR

Cat English grew up on a council estate in Greater Manchester and isn't ashamed of where she came from. It made her who she is today. A voice for the animals, the wilder the better. She now lives in the West Pennines with her beau (and her forty-something rescued feral cats who think it's playtime when the lights go out). She will hold the door open for royalty and will keep that door held open for the homeless person walking behind them.

Cat carried out her work experience in Waterstones bookshop where she openly admits she was drawn to the Karma Sutra section–it was no surprise then that she swapped her retail management shoes for stilettos as a high-class call girl on her path to becoming the 'Mother Teresa of cats'.